Everyday Mathematics®

The University of Chicago School Mathematics Project

Assessment Handbook

Kindergarten

Wright Group

The McGraw·Hill Companies

The University of Chicago School Mathematics Project (UCSMP)

Max Bell, Director, UCSMP Elementary Materials Component; Director, *Everyday Mathematics*
First Edition
James McBride, Director, *Everyday Mathematics* Second Edition
Andy Isaacs, Director, *Everyday Mathematics* Third Edition
Amy Dillard, Associate Director, *Everyday Mathematics* Third Edition

Authors

Jean Bell, William M. Carroll[†], Amy Dillard[*], Deborah Arron Leslie[*], Kathleen Pitvorec

[†] *First Edition only*
[*] *Third Edition only*

Third Edition Early Childhood Team Leaders

David W. Beer, Deborah Arron Leslie

Teachers in Residence

Ann E. Audrain, Dorothy Freedman, Margaret Krulee, Barbara Smart

Editorial Assistant

Patrick Carroll

Contributors

David W. Beer, Mary Ellen Dairyko, Sharon Draznin, Nancy Hanvey, Laurie Leff, Denise Porter, Herb Price, Joyce Timmons, Lisa Winters

Photo Credits

©Brand X Pictures/Jupiterimages, cover, *right;* ©Willard R. Culver/Getty Images, cover, *center;* ©Getty Images, cover, *background, back cover.*

Permissions

The quotes on pages 4, 5, and 8 are reprinted with permission from *Knowing What Students Know: The Science and Design of Educational Assessment* © 2001 by the National Academy of Sciences, courtesy of the National Academies Press, Washington, D.C.

---

www.WrightGroup.com

Wright Group

Send all inquiries to:
Wright Group/McGraw-Hill
P.O. Box 812960
Chicago, IL 60681

ISBN 0-07-604528-5

8 9 MAZ 12 11 10 09 08

The *McGraw-Hill* Companies

Contents

Assessment Masters 76

Philosophy of Assessment in *Everyday Mathematics*®

Introduction

Too often, school assessment tends to provide only scattered snapshots of student achievement rather than continuous records of growth. In *Everyday Mathematics,* assessment is like a motion picture, revealing the development of each child's mathematical understanding over time while also giving the teacher useful feedback about the instructional needs of individual children and the class.

For assessment to be useful to teachers, children, parents, and others, the *Everyday Mathematics* authors believe that . . .

◆ Teachers need to have a variety of assessment tools and techniques to choose from so children can demonstrate what they know in a variety of ways and teachers can have reliable information from multiple sources.

◆ Children should be included in the assessment process. Self assessment and reflection are skills children will develop over time if they are encouraged.

◆ Assessment and instruction should be closely aligned. Assessment should assist teachers in making instructional decisions concerning individual children and the class.

◆ Assessment should focus on all important outcomes, not only on outcomes that are easy to measure.

◆ A good assessment program makes instruction easier.

◆ The best assessment plans are developed by teachers working collaboratively within their schools and districts.

Everyday Mathematics offers many opportunities for assessing children's knowledge and skills. This handbook describes the *Kindergarten Everyday Mathematics* assessment resources and serves as a guide for navigating through those resources and helping you design and implement a balanced classroom assessment plan.

Balanced Assessment

When planning a balanced assessment, begin by asking several basic questions:

◆ *What are the purposes of assessment?*

◆ *What are the contexts for assessment?*

◆ *What are the sources of evidence for assessment?*

◆ *What content is assessed?*

What Are the Purposes of Assessment?

The purposes of assessment serve three main functions: to support learning, to measure achievement, and to evaluate programs. Each purpose is integral to achieving a balanced assessment plan.

Formative assessment supports learning by providing information about children's current knowledge and abilities so that you can plan future instruction more effectively. Formative assessment encourages children to identify their areas of weakness or strength so they can focus their efforts more precisely.

Summative assessment measures children's growth and achievement. A summative assessment might be designed, for example, to determine whether children have learned certain material by the end of a fixed period of study.

Program evaluation means judging how well a program is working. A school district, for example, may want to identify schools with especially strong mathematics programs so their successes can be replicated in other schools with weaker programs. Program evaluation makes this possible.

Assessment tools and techniques often serve more than one purpose. Assessments built into a curriculum might give teachers information they can use both to plan future instruction more effectively or to prepare progress reports. District administrators might use this information to allocate professional development resources.

Purposes of Assessment

Formative Assessment	Summative Assessment	Program Evaluation
◆ Used to plan instruction ◆ Helps students to reflect on their progress	◆ Used to measure student growth and achievement ◆ Helps determine if students have learned content	◆ Used to evaluate overall success of the math program

What Are the Contexts for Assessment?

Assessment occurs in a variety of contexts.

◆ **Ongoing assessment** involves gathering information from children's everyday work. These assessments can take place at the same time as regular classroom instruction.

◆ **Periodic assessment** consists of formal assessments that are built into a curriculum, such as the Baseline, Mid-Year, and End-of-Year tasks on pages 40–48 of this book.

◆ **External assessment** is independent of the curriculum. An example of an external assessment is a standardized test.

Everyday Mathematics supports all three contexts of assessment, and it provides tools and materials for ongoing and periodic assessments that you can use to create a balanced assessment plan.

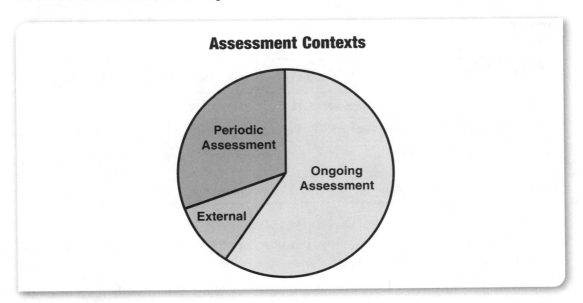

The size of the sections of the circle in the figure above are meant to be suggestive, but the exact proportions of ongoing, periodic, and external assessments will vary depending on your grade level, the time of year, state and district mandates, and many other factors.

What Are the Sources of Evidence for Assessment?

> *Assessment is a process of reasoning from evidence.*
>
> (Pellegrino, Chudowsky, and Glaser 2001, 36)

The evidence for assessing what children know is indirect because we cannot know exactly what they are thinking. Evidence about children's knowledge and capabilities comes from observing them while they are actively engaged and also from analyzing the products of their work. Whatever conclusions we may make about children's thinking must be based on **observations** or **products.**

The table below shows the different contexts for assessment and the sources of evidence used for each context. Specific assessment tasks in *Everyday Mathematics* are included. Use this table as a guide in designing your balanced assessment plan.

Sources of Evidence and Assessment Contexts

	Assessment Contexts		
Sources	**Ongoing Assessment**	**Periodic Assessment**	**External Assessment**
Observation	◆ "Kid-Watching"	◆ Oral Assessments	◆ Observations by outside experts
Product	◆ Written Work	◆ Written Assessments	◆ Standardized tests

Each context for assessment (ongoing, periodic, or external) can yield evidence either through observations or products.

◆ Observing children as they are doing their daily work can provide a great deal of information about their understandings, skills, and dispositions; this kind of ongoing observational assessment may be considered "kid-watching."

◆ A written assessment that is included as part of a curriculum is an example of a periodic product assessment.

◆ A classroom visit by an outside expert who will observe particular children is an example of an external assessment using observational evidence.

What Content Is Assessed?

> *Assessment does not exist in isolation, but must be closely aligned with the goals of curriculum and instruction.*
>
> (Pellegrino, Chudowsky, and Glaser, 2001, 36)

In recent years, national organizations and most states have issued detailed sets of learning goals and standards, which provide useful guidance about what content is important to learn and, therefore, important to assess. Aligning assessment, curriculum, and instruction with standards and goals increases coherence in the system and produces better outcomes. To help teachers understand the structure of *Everyday Mathematics* and therefore better understand what to assess, the authors developed Program Goals, which are organized by content strand and carefully articulated across the grades. Below are the six content strands and their related Program Goals:

Everyday Mathematics Program Goals

Number and Numeration
- Understand the meanings, uses, and representations of numbers
- Understand equivalent names for numbers
- Understand common numerical relations

Operations and Computation
- Compute accurately
- Make reasonable estimates
- Understand meanings of operations

Data and Chance
- Select and create appropriate graphical representations of collected or given data
- Analyze and interpret data
- Understand and apply basic concepts of probability

Measurement and Reference Frames
- Understand the systems and processes of measurement; use appropriate techniques, tools, units, and formulas in making measurements
- Use and understand reference frames

Geometry
- Investigate characteristics and properties of two- and three-dimensional geometric shapes
- Apply transformations and symmetry in geometric situations

Patterns, Functions, and Algebra
- Understand patterns and functions
- Use algebraic notation to represent and analyze situations and structures

Program Goals are threads that weave the curriculum together across grades. "Compute accurately," for example, is a Program Goal. Children in *Everyday Mathematics* are expected to compute accurately. The expectations for a child achieving this goal in Grade 2 are obviously different from what is expected from a student in Grade 6. For this reason, the Program Goals are further refined through Grade-Level Goals.

Grade-Level Goals are guideposts along trajectories of learning that span multiple years. They are the big ideas at each grade level; they do not capture all of the content covered. The Grade-Level Goals describe how *Everyday Mathematics* builds mastery over time—first through informal exposure, later through more formal instruction, and finally through application. Because the Grade-Level Goals are cumulative, it is essential for children to experience the complete curriculum at each grade level. The example below shows the development of Grade-Level Goals for addition and subtraction procedures.

Grade K	Use manipulatives, number lines, and mental arithmetic to solve problems involving the addition and subtraction of single-digit whole numbers.
Grade 1	Use manipulatives, number grids, tally marks, mental arithmetic, and calculators to solve problems involving the addition and subtraction of 1-digit or 2-digit whole numbers; calculate and compare the values of combinations of coins.
Grade 2	Use manipulatives, number grids, tally marks, mental arithmetic, paper & pencil, and calculators to solve problems involving the addition and subtraction of 2-digit whole numbers; describe the strategies used; calculate and compare values of coin and bill combinations.
Grade 3	Use manipulatives, mental arithmetic, paper-and-pencil algorithms, and calculators to solve problems involving the addition and subtraction of whole numbers and decimals in a money context; describe the strategies used and explain how they work.
Grade 4	Use manipulatives, mental arithmetic, paper-and-pencil algorithms, and calculators to solve problems involving the addition and subtraction of whole numbers and decimals through hundredths; describe the strategies used and explain how they work.
Grade 5	Use mental arithmetic, paper-and-pencil algorithms, and calculators to solve problems involving the addition and subtraction of whole numbers, decimals, and signed numbers; describe the strategies used and explain how they work.
Grade 6	Use mental arithmetic, paper-and-pencil algorithms, and calculators to solve problems involving addition and subtraction of whole numbers, decimals, and signed numbers; describe the strategies used and explain how they work.

All assessment opportunities in *Everyday Mathematics* are linked to specific Grade-Level Goals. The curriculum is designed so that the vast majority of children will reach the Grade-Level Goals for a given grade upon completion of that grade and as a result will be well prepared to succeed in higher levels of mathematics. The complete list of Program Goals and Grade-Level Goals begins on page 27 of this handbook.

Creating a Balanced Assessment Plan

In *Everyday Mathematics,* assessment is primarily designed to help you

◆ learn about children's current knowledge and abilities so that you can plan future instruction more effectively—formative assessment; and
◆ measure children's progress toward and achievement of Grade-Level Goals—summative assessment.

Although there is no one right assessment plan for all classrooms, all assessment plans should provide a balance of assessment sources from different contexts. See the chart on page 4 of this handbook for specific assessment tasks in *Everyday Mathematics* that support the different sources and contexts.

Planning Tips

Do not try to use all the assessment resources at once. Instead, devise a manageable, balanced plan. Choose those tools and techniques that best match your teaching style and your children's needs.

Consider the following guidelines:

◆ Start small.
◆ Incorporate assessment into your daily class routine.
◆ Set up an easy and efficient record-keeping system.
◆ Personalize and adapt the plan as the year progresses.

Your assessment plan should be designed to answer these questions:

◆ How is the class doing?
◆ How are individual students doing?
◆ How do I need to adjust instruction to meet children's needs?
◆ How can I communicate to children, parents, and others about the progress being made?

The following sections of this handbook provide further details about the tools and techniques you can use to develop a balanced assessment plan. Beginning on page 35, you will find descriptions of periodic assessment opportunities, assessment overviews by section, and assessment overviews by mathematical topic strands. Using these tools, you can support student learning, improve your instruction, measure student growth and achievement, and make the most of your experience with *Everyday Mathematics.*

Ongoing Assessment

An integral part of a balanced assessment plan involves gathering information from children's everyday work. Opportunities for collecting ongoing assessment in the form of observations and products are highlighted in *Everyday Mathematics* through Informing Instruction and Recognizing Student Achievement notes. In addition to these opportunities, your everyday observations of children using mathematics throughout the classroom ("kid-watching") will provide a great deal of meaningful ongoing assessment information.

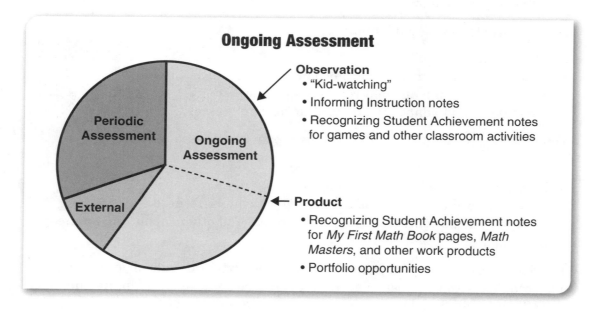

Ongoing Assessment: Kid-Watching

Everyday "kid-watching" throughout the day is one of the most important ongoing assessment techniques for Kindergarten, because mathematics permeates the Kindergarten classroom, and because paper-and-pencil tasks are not the best way for Kindergartners to show what they know. Teachers of young children glean a great deal of anecdotal assessment information about children's mathematical interests, skills, understanding, and difficulties from watching children and listening to their comments and questions during activities and group times, in the Math Center and other areas of the classroom. The Ongoing Daily Routines are an excellent source of kid-watching assessment information. See pages 66–75 for specific suggestions about using kid-watching to gather assessment information related to each Kindergarten Goal. See pages 16–20 for some suggestions to help you manage and record your kid-watching observations.

Ongoing Assessment: Informing Instruction

Informing Instruction notes are designed to help you anticipate and recognize common errors and misconceptions in children's thinking and alert you to multiple solution strategies or unique insights that children may offer. These notes suggest how to use observations of children's work to effectively adapt instruction.

Sample 1 - Informing Instruction

Ongoing Assessment:
Informing Instruction

Watch for children who are unable to visually discriminate between shapes. Try to work one on one with these children to help them find pictures to add to the collage. Children who are having difficulty may benefit from additional tactile and kinesthetic experiences with shapes.

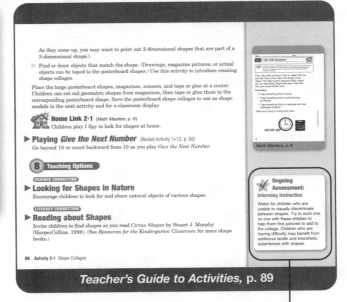

Teacher's Guide to Activities, p. 89

As indicated, the Informing Instruction notes can be found in the margin area of the *Teacher's Guide to Activities.*

Ongoing Assessment: Recognizing Student Achievement

Recognizing Student Achievement notes highlight specific tasks that teachers can use for assessment to monitor children's progress toward Grade-Level Goals.

These tasks include the following:

◆ Core Activities (Main activity or Revisit activity),
◆ Teaching Options,
◆ *Everyday Mathematics* games,
◆ *My First Math Book* pages, and
◆ Other work samples (completed *Math Masters* pages, drawings, number stories, and so on)

Each Recognizing Student Achievement note identifies the task from which to gather information, the concept or skill to be assessed, and the expectations for a child who is *making adequate progress* toward meeting the specific Grade-Level Goal.

Sample - Recognizing Student Achievement

Ongoing Assessment:
Recognizing Student Achievement

Use **Shapes by Feel** to assess children's ability to name shapes and describe some of their attributes. Children are making adequate progress if they correctly identify and name a triangle and a circle. Some children may be able to recognize the difference between squares and rectangles.

[Geometry Goal 1]

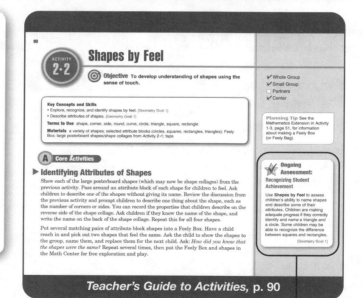

Teacher's Guide to Activities, p. 90

As indicated, the Recognizing Student Achievement notes can be found in the margin area of the *Teacher's Guide to Activities.*

The Recognizing Student Achievement tasks were chosen with the expectation that the majority of children will be successful with them. Children who are *making adequate progress* as defined by a Recognizing Student Achievement task are on a trajectory to meet the corresponding Grade-Level Goal. Some children may go beyond the identified expectations of the highlighted task and are ready to further explore or apply concepts.

In *Kindergarten Everyday Mathematics,* Recognizing Student Achievement tasks provide information that may help determine which Teaching Options to use in your classroom. Many activities include suggestions for Readiness activities or Enrichment activities to meet individual children's needs, although most of the Teaching Options are appropriate for all children and will serve to enhance their learning of the skills or concepts in the main activity.

The information you learn from the Recognizing Student Achievement tasks may also help you determine how to present the Revisit activities. In some cases, you might present the activity just as you did earlier in the year. In others, you might vary it to reflect children's progress since its introduction.

Portfolios

Portfolios are a versatile tool for children's assessment. They help children reflect on their mathematical growth and help you to understand and document that growth. Portfolios are part of a balanced assessment plan in that they

◆ emphasize progress over time.

◆ involve children more directly in the assessment process, as they participate in selecting work and explaining what the work demonstrates.

◆ document both strengths and weaknesses in a child's mathematical development.

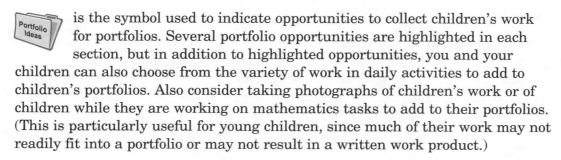 is the symbol used to indicate opportunities to collect children's work for portfolios. Several portfolio opportunities are highlighted in each section, but in addition to highlighted opportunities, you and your children can also choose from the variety of work in daily activities to add to children's portfolios. Also consider taking photographs of children's work or of children while they are working on mathematics tasks to add to their portfolios. (This is particularly useful for young children, since much of their work may not readily fit into a portfolio or may not result in a written work product.)

Consider taking dictation from children about their selected works. An optional master, *Good Work!,* is provided on page 103 and can be used to encourage children's self-reflection about their portfolio entries.

You may also ask parents to complete a *Parent Reflections* page (*Assessment Handbook,* page 104) for inclusion in children's portfolios.

Periodic Assessment

Periodic assessments are another key component of a balanced assessment plan. The figure below lists the various periodic assessment tasks provided in *Kindergarten Everyday Mathematics*.

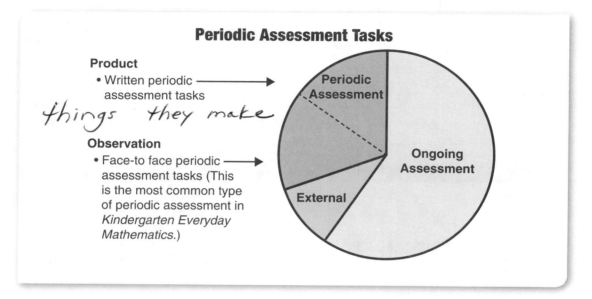

Periodic Assessment Tasks

Product
• Written periodic assessment tasks

things they make

Observation
• Face-to face periodic assessment tasks (This is the most common type of periodic assessment in *Kindergarten Everyday Mathematics*.)

Periodic Assessment

Ongoing Assessment

External

Baseline, Mid-Year, and End-of-Year Assessments

Kindergarten Everyday Mathematics suggests various periodic assessment tasks for the beginning, middle, and end of the school year. These periodic assessments help you take stock of where individual children are in their mathematical development at specific times during the school year. You can use this information for both formative and summative purposes to

◆ tailor instruction to the needs of individuals and the whole group.

◆ complete the assessment picture that is generated from ongoing assessment.

◆ help communicate progress to parents on report cards or during parent-teacher conferences.

Although many of the Baseline, Mid-Year, and End-of-Year periodic assessment tasks described in this book are more formal than the ongoing assessment suggestions, many of them can be integrated into your regular classroom activities. Most of the tasks work best when conducted with individuals or small groups of children. See pages 36–48, for specific suggestions for Baseline, Mid-Year, and End-of-Year assessment tasks that correlate to the Kindergarten Goals.

External Assessment

Outside tests, one example of external assessment, are generally tests given at the school, district, or state level, or are nationally-standardized tests. Most teachers are familiar with the standardized tests that have multiple-choice responses. The frustrating aspect of this type of test is that it analyzes a narrow range of mathematical thinking and does not assess the depth and breadth of the mathematical knowledge that should be attained in a well-implemented *Everyday Mathematics* classroom.

More recently, some district and state tests have included performance assessments or open-ended components. *Everyday Mathematics* presents varied mathematics tasks that prepare children for these testing situations: problems requiring children to explain their thinking and prompts designed to help children explore content more deeply. If you have a choice in your district, encourage the use of these performance-based or open-ended assessments. They better depict the depth of your children's understandings, as well as their abilities to communicate mathematically, solve problems, and reason.

Performance-based assessments developed at the school or district level probably provide the best opportunities to gather information about student achievement in local classrooms. Teams of teachers and administrators can develop assessments and rubrics that enhance the learning process, rather than focus on narrow thinking used only in a small portion of mathematical activities. At some grade levels, these assessments can be used exclusively. When standardized testing is mandatory at a certain grade level, performance-based assessments can provide a better picture of the mathematical education occurring in the classroom than other types of standardized tests.

Record-Keeping

If you teach *Kindergarten Everyday Mathematics* as intended and use the techniques described in this book, you will have a vast amount of information about children's mathematical skills and understanding. This section of the handbook offers several tools to help you organize and record this store of information. Pick and choose the suggestions that work for you.

Collecting and Organizing Ongoing-Assessment Information

Observing children during regular classroom interactions—as they work independently or in groups—is a very important assessment technique for Kindergarten. However, keeping track of these observations can be difficult. The following suggestions are intended to help you find ways to keep records of your ongoing assessment efforts in a manageable and unobtrusive way. You might try out one or more of the recording techniques described. Feel free to adapt them to work in your classroom as needed.

Flip-Card Collection Some teachers attach index cards to a clipboard for recording observations. To do this, use one card for each child. You might use one color for the first five cards, a second color for the next five cards, and so on. Focus on recording observations of one group of five children each day, along with any other anecdotal observations of the rest of the children. Try to observe each child at least every two weeks. Be sure to date your observations.

David
Andy
Kathy
Peter
Ebony
Martine
Jacob
Jean
Juan
Kevin
Erin
Colleen
Diane
May

Steve
Tom
Sarah
Cassandra
Ken
Seline
Héctor
Yosh
Claire
Kyesha
Galena
Charlotte
Dan
Carlos

After a child's index card has become filled with information, remove it and file it alphabetically. Tape a new card to the clipboard to continue the process. The completed cards will help you keep track of children's needs and the implications for instruction, as well as prepare for parent conferences.

Computer Labels Print the children's names on sheets of large peel-off computer address labels. Write observations on each child's label. As labels become filled, place them on cards or in a notebook for individual children.

Class Progress Indicators The Class Progress Indicator on page 105 is useful for compiling and organizing class data for any assessment task, concept, or skill. To use the Class Progress Indicator, write the task, concept, or skill ("Count on by 1s," for example) at the beginning of a row on the table. Then write children's names in the appropriate column according to their performance on that task. Choose appropriate benchmarks to categorize children's performance for each task (for example: "does not yet count to 30;" "counts to 30;" and "counts well beyond 30"). Looking at class data in this way may help you plan and tailor instruction by choosing appropriate teaching options, creating small groups for particular activities, modifying questions during activities, and so on.

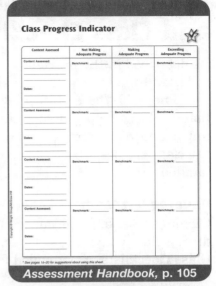

Assessment Handbook, p. 105

Observation Sheets You might make a copy of the blank Observation Sheet on page 107 for each child and record ongoing observations on the sheet, much as you would on the index cards or computer labels described previously. Save the sheets for each child in a file folder to help you review for parent conferences and plan and individualize instruction.

Assessment Handbook, p. 107

Observational Class Checklists You might use copies of the blank Class Checklist master on page 106 for recording ongoing observations and interactions. Write children's names on the rows, and add particular activities, concepts, or skills that you want to observe to the column heads. You can make notes in the appropriate space as you observe children at work.

NOTE After you have written children's names in the rows, make several copies of the checklist master so you won't have to rewrite children's names on each checklist you use. This allows you to change the order of the children's names without changing the column headings.

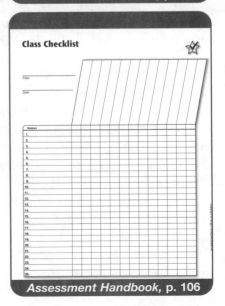

Assessment Handbook, p. 106

Individual Profiles of Progress and Class Checklists

As described in the previous sections, a wealth of assessment information can be collected from kid-watching, using Recognizing Achievement notes, and the Baseline, Mid-Year, and End-of-Year periodic assessment tasks suggested in this handbook. To help you keep track of children's progress in areas that are important to your school and district, various checklists for individuals and for the class are described below and are provided beginning on page 77 of this handbook.

Ongoing Assessment Tools

Ongoing assessment is generally conducted during class activities, so Ongoing Assessment Class Checklists are provided for recording information gathered from everyday kid-watching and from the Recognizing Student Achievement notes in activities. There are 4 class checklists for ongoing assessment: one each for Sections 1 and 2, Sections 3 and 4, Sections 5 and 6, and Sections 7 and 8. For each Recognizing Student Achievement note, the checklists identify the activity number, the content assessed, and the related Kindergarten Goal. They also include a column to record information collected from everyday kid-watching or other comments or notes. (See "Collecting and Organizing Ongoing Assessment Information" on page 16 for additional suggestions about collecting and recording information from everyday kid-watching.) If desired, ongoing assessment information can be transferred from the class checklists to an ongoing assessment Individual Profile of Progress for each child.

Assessment Handbook, p. 78

Alternately, you can enter ongoing assessment information for each child directly onto a Cumulative Individual Profile of Progress (see next page).

Periodic Assessment Tools

Most of the Baseline, Mid-Year, and End-of-Year periodic assessment tasks will be conducted with individuals or small groups of students. In addition to recording specific information about how each child performs on each task (how high they count, which shapes they identify, and so on), it is a good idea to document notes about children's approaches to the tasks, their strategies, whether they found particular tasks very easy or very difficult, and so on. All of this information will be very useful in describing where a child is in his or her mathematical development at that point in time. To facilitate detailed record-keeping about the periodic assessments, Individual Profile of Progress sheets for the Baseline, Mid-Year, and End-of-Year periodic assessment tasks are included on pages 85, 87–88, and 91–94. Make a copy of each record sheet for each child. You can write results and notes on the sheet as you conduct the periodic assessment tasks with individuals or small groups.

Alternately, you can enter periodic assessment information for each child directly onto a Cumulative Individual Profile of Progress (see below).

If whole-class data is needed (for communicating with administrators, for example), you might transfer information from the Individual Profile of Progress sheets to a Baseline, Mid-Year, or End-of-Year Class Checklist.

Cumulative Individual Profiles of Progress

To show a more complete picture of assessment data from various sources and points in time, you can compile information from ongoing and periodic assessment onto a Cumulative Individual Profile of Progress for each child. There are 2 Cumulative Individual Profiles of Progress forms. The first form (see pages 97–98) covers Sections 1–4 and includes Recognizing Student Achievement opportunities from these sections as well as Baseline and Mid-Year periodic assessment tasks. The second form (see pages 99–102) covers Sections 5–8 and includes Recognizing Student Achievement opportunities from these sections as well as Mid-Year and End-of-Year periodic assessment tasks. Cumulative Individual Profiles of Progress are excellent for sharing with parents and next year's teachers, and for placing in children's portfolios.

Assessment Handbook, p. 87

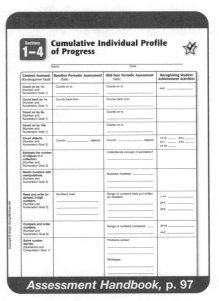

Assessment Handbook, p. 97

Options for Recording Data on Checklists

There are a variety of possible record-keeping schemes for Individual Profiles of Progress and Class Checklists. For many skills or concepts, it is most informative to record a specific piece of information, such as how high a child counts or which shapes she recognizes. In other cases, you may want to indicate whether children are making adequate progress toward the related Grade-Level Goal with a recording system such as the following:

+ or A	Child is *making adequate progress* toward Grade-Level Goal.
– or N	Child is *not making adequate progress* toward Grade-Level Goal.

NOTE Each Recognizing Student Achievement note in the *Teacher's Guide to Activities* and all of the Mid-Year and End-of-Year periodic assessment tasks on pages 42–48 of this handbook include expectations for making adequate progress.

Also feel free to devise your own system for record-keeping on the individual and class checklists.

Assessment Management System

Introduction

The *Everyday Mathematics* Assessment Management System is an electronic tool that assists educators in monitoring and documenting children's progress toward meeting *Everyday Mathematics* Grade-Level Goals.

Record-Keeping

You can use the tool to enter student performance information for the following *Everyday Mathematics* assessments:

◆ Ongoing Assessment: Recognizing Student Achievement
◆ Periodic Assessment: Baseline, Mid-Year, and End-of-Year Tasks

You can also easily complement the assessments provided in *Everyday Mathematics* by adding student performance data from everyday kid-watching, tasks you design, or from the many other tasks in the *Everyday Mathematics* curriculum.

Features

The *Assessment Management System* includes many features for supporting your balanced assessment plan. *For example:*

◆ All of the suggested *Everyday Mathematics* assessment tasks are built into the system. Clicking an activity number will bring you directly to the corresponding assessment task.
◆ As long as you assign a Grade-Level Goal to the assessment task, any other tasks that you create or that you use from the curriculum are incorporated into the system.
◆ A variety of data-entry options allow you to record general student performance and text comments for each of your children. You can determine the level of specificity that best suits your assessment needs.

When you track student progress on a Recognizing Student Achievement task, you can view a description of the task and the corresponding Grade-Level Goal.

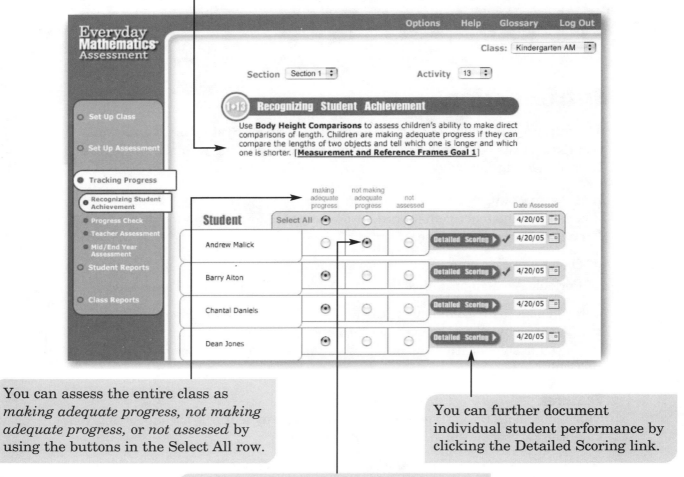

You can assess the entire class as *making adequate progress, not making adequate progress,* or *not assessed* by using the buttons in the Select All row.

You can further document individual student performance by clicking the Detailed Scoring link.

Additionally, you can also assess individual students as *making adequate progress, not making adequate progress,* or *not assessed.*

Student Reports

Once you have entered student assessment data, the *Assessment Management System* provides you with a variety of ways to sort and organize the information. *For example:*

◆ Class and individual reports show student performance data on specific assessment tasks.

◆ Class and individual reports show student performance data sorted by content strand, Program Goal, or Grade-Level Goal.

◆ Class and individual reports are based on time frames that you create, which allows you to tailor the reports to correspond with your district's marking periods.

These reports can then be viewed electronically or printed for distribution.

Monitor Student Progress

Everyday Mathematics was designed so that the vast majority of children will reach the Grade-Level Goals for a given grade upon completion of that grade. Each assessment task provides a snapshot of a child's progress toward the corresponding Grade-Level Goal. Taken together, these snapshots form a moving picture that can help teachers assess whether a child is on a trajectory or path to meet the Grade-Level Goal.

The *Assessment Management System* is a valuable tool for managing the tremendous flow of information about student performance. By viewing the reports, you can determine whether or not children have successfully accomplished what is expected of them up to that point in the curriculum. Furthermore, reports display future assessment tasks for a given Grade-Level Goal. This function allows you to see additional assessment opportunities coming up so you can monitor student progress toward specific goals.

Grading Assistance

While grading is not the primary goal of the *Assessment Management System,* the tool can assist you in assigning grades. The *Assessment Management System* allows you to sort and view student performance on assessment tasks by content strand, Program Goal, and Grade-Level Goal so that you can keep documented evidence of the performance. Additionally, the *Assessment Management System* allows you to monitor student progress on many types of assessment tasks, including those that you create so your evidence for assessment is based on multiple sources. These records of student performance, combined with the careful observations you make about your children's work, will help you assign fair and accurate grades.

Online User Instructions and Help

For assistance with the *Assessment Management System* and specific feature instructions, click the Help link at the top of any screen within the tool. Text and animated instructions have been included to help you smoothly incorporate the *Assessment Management System* into your balanced assessment plan.

Frequently Asked Questions

1. **Do the Grade-Level Goals summarize all of the concepts and skills that are covered each year?**

   No. Although the Grade-Level Goals reflect the core of the curriculum at each grade level, they are not comprehensive. They do not capture all of the content that is addressed each year. Nor are they a list of activities that are completed each year. Some grade-level content supports future Grade-Level Goals that are not articulated at the given grade level.

2. **With all of these Grade-Level Goals, how will I know when I'm just exposing children to a new concept or skill?**

   The *Everyday Mathematics* curriculum aims for proficiency with concepts and skills through repeated exposures over several years. The *Teacher's Guide to Activities* alerts teachers to content that is being introduced for the first time through Links to the Future notes. These notes usually provide specific references to future Grade-Level Goals and help teachers understand introductory activities at their grade levels in the context of the entire K–6 curriculum.

   All the content in *Everyday Mathematics* is important, whether it's being experienced for the first or the fifth time. The *Everyday Mathematics* curriculum is similar to an intricately woven rug, with many threads that appear and reappear to form complex patterns. Different children will progress at different rates, so multiple exposures to important content are critical for accommodating individual differences. The program was created so that it is consistent with how children actually learn mathematics. It builds understanding over a period of time, first through informal exposure, and later through more formal and directed instruction. For children to succeed, they need the opportunity to experience all that the curriculum has to offer in every grade.

3. **There are a lot of activities in my grade-level materials. Do I have to finish all of the activities in the program at my grade level?**

   Everyday Mathematics was created to be consistent with how children actually learn mathematics, building understanding over time, first through informal exposure and later through more formal instruction. Because the Grade-Level Goals are cumulative, it is essential for children to experience the complete curriculum at each grade level.

4. **Do I need to keep track of progress on Program Goals?**

   Program Goals are the threads that weave the content together across grade levels and form the skeleton of the curriculum. The Program Goals are further refined through the Grade-Level Goals. *Everyday Mathematics* provides a variety of tools you can use to assess children's progress on the Grade-Level Goals throughout the year. Because every Grade-Level Goal is related to a Program Goal, you are gathering information at this less-specific level as well. This allows great flexibility in reporting to parents. Depending on how your district requires you to aggregate data, you can look broadly at strands, more closely at Program Goals, or specifically at Grade-Level Goals using the suggested assessments in *Everyday Mathematics*.

5. **What do the authors mean by "adequate progress"?**

Children who are *making adequate progress* as defined by a Recognizing Student Achievement note are on a trajectory to meet the Grade-Level Goal. Such children have successfully accomplished what is expected up to that point in the curriculum. If children continue to progress as expected, then they will demonstrate proficiency with the Grade-Level Goal upon completion of the year.

The performance expectations described in the Recognizing Student Achievement notes for any given Grade-Level Goal progress developmentally throughout the year. The level of performance that is expected in October is not the same as that which is expected in April. The term *adequate progress* describes the level of competency the majority of children can be expected to have at a particular time. The authors of *Everyday Mathematics* chose the Recognizing Student Achievement tasks with the expectation that the majority of children would be successful with them, which is in line with the expectation that the vast majority of children will successfully reach the Grade-Level Goals for their grade level.

Of course, it is important to recognize that young children often develop in uneven bursts, so it is impossible to set precise points along the way to a given goal. The *adequate progress* markers should be used simply as a guide.

6. **Can I use only the periodic assessments to collect assessment information?**

Everyday Mathematics includes a variety of assessment tasks to ensure that all children have sufficient opportunity to demonstrate what they know. Some children best demonstrate their knowledge through performance tasks, some through explanations and demonstrations, and some through pencil-and-paper tasks or other work products. The assessment tasks in the program have been chosen to accommodate a range of learners. Using any one tool might limit what you are able to learn about your children.

Recommended Reading

Black, Paul, and Dylan Wiliam. "Assessment and Classroom Learning." *Assessment in Education* (March, 1998): 7–74.

———. "Inside the Black Box: Raising Standards Through Classroom Assessment." *Phi Delta Kappan* 80, no. 2 (October, 1998): 139–149.

Bryant, Brian R., and Teddy Maddox. "Using Alternative Assessment Techniques to Plan and Evaluate Mathematics." *LD Forum 21,* no. 2 (winter, 1996): 24–33.

Eisner, Elliot W. "The Uses and Limits of Performance Assessment." *Phi Delta Kappan* 80, no. 9 (May, 1999): 658–661.

Kulm, Gerald. *Mathematics Assessment: What Works in the Classroom.* San Francisco: Jossey-Bass Publishers, 1994.

National Council of Teachers of Mathematics (NCTM). *Curriculum and Evaluation Standards for School Mathematics.* Reston, VA: NCTM, 1989.

———. *Assessment Standards for School Mathematics.* Reston, VA: NCTM, 1995.

———. *Principles and Standards for School Mathematics.* Reston, VA: NCTM, 2000.

National Research Council. Committee on the Foundations of Assessment. Pellegrino, James W., Naomi Chudowsky, and Robert Glaser, eds. *Knowing What Students Know: The Science and Design of Educational Assessment.* Washington, DC: National Academy Press, 2001.

National Research Council, Mathematical Sciences Education Board. *Measuring What Counts: A Conceptual Guide for Mathematics Assessment.* Washington, D.C.: National Academy Press, 1993.

Pearson, Bethyl, and Cathy Berghoff. "London Bridge Is Not Falling Down: It's Supporting Alternative Assessment." *TESOL Journal* 5, no. 4 (summer, 1996): 28–31.

Shepard, Lorrie A. "Using Assessment to Improve Learning." *Educational Leadership* 52, no. 5 (February, 1995): 38–43.

Stenmark, Jean Kerr, ed. *Mathematics Assessment: Myths, Models, Good Questions, and Practical Suggestions.* Reston, VA: National Council of Teachers of Mathematics, 1991.

Stiggens, Richard J. *Student-Centered Classroom Assessment.* Englewood Cliffs, NJ: Prentice-Hall, 1997.

Webb, N. L., and A. F. Coxford, eds. *Assessment in the Mathematics Classroom: 1993 Yearbook.* Reston, VA: National Council of Teachers of Mathematics, 1993.
http://everydaymath.uchicago.edu

Everyday Mathematics K–2 Goals Tables

Strand: NUMBER AND NUMERATION			
Content	**Kindergarten**	**First Grade**	**Second Grade**
Program Goal: Understand the meanings, uses, and representations of numbers.			
Rote counting	**Goal 1.** Count on by 1s to 100; count on by 2s, 5s, and 10s and count back by 1s with number grids, number lines, and calculators.	**Goal 1.** Count on by 1s, 2s, 5s, and 10s past 100 and back by 1s from any number less than 100 with and without number grids, number lines, and calculators.	**Goal 1.** Count on by 1s, 2s, 5s, 10s, 25s, and 100s past 1,000 and back by 1s from any number less than 1,000 with and without number grids, number lines, and calculators.
Rational counting	**Goal 2.** Count 20 or more objects; estimate the number of objects in a collection.	**Goal 2.** Count collections of objects accurately and reliably; estimate the number of objects in a collection.	
Place value and notation	**Goal 3.** Model numbers with manipulatives; use manipulatives to exchange 1s for 10s and 10s for 100s; recognize that digits can be used and combined to read and write numbers; read numbers up to 30.	**Goal 3.** Read, write, and model with manipulatives whole numbers up to 1,000; identify places in such numbers and the values of the digits in those places.	**Goal 2.** Read, write, and model with manipulatives whole numbers up to 10,000; identify places in such numbers and the values of the digits in those places; read and write money amounts in dollars-and-cents notation.

Content	Kindergarten	First Grade	Second Grade
Program Goal: Understand the meanings, uses, and representations of numbers. *cont.*			
Meanings and uses of fractions	**Goal 4.** Use manipulatives to model half of a region or a collection; describe the model.	**Goal 4.** Use manipulatives and drawings to model halves, thirds, and fourths as equal parts of a region or a collection; describe the model.	**Goal 3.** Use manipulatives and drawings to model fractions as equal parts of a region or a collection; describe the models and name the fractions.
Number theory		**Goal 5.** Use manipulatives to identify and model odd and even numbers.	**Goal 4.** Recognize numbers as odd or even.
Program Goal: Understand equivalent names for numbers.			
Equivalent names for whole numbers	**Goal 5.** Use manipulatives, drawings, and numerical expressions involving addition and subtraction of 1-digit numbers to give equivalent names for whole numbers up to 20.	**Goal 6.** Use manipulatives, drawings, tally marks, and numerical expressions involving addition and subtraction of 1- or 2-digit numbers to give equivalent names for whole numbers up to 100.	**Goal 5.** Use tally marks, arrays, and numerical expressions involving addition and subtraction to give equivalent names for whole numbers.
Equivalent names for fractions, decimals, and percents			**Goal 6.** Use manipulatives and drawings to model equivalent names for $\frac{1}{2}$.
Program Goal: Understand common numerical relations.			
Comparing and ordering numbers	**Goal 6.** Compare and order whole numbers up to 20.	**Goal 7.** Compare and order whole numbers up to 1,000.	**Goal 7.** Compare and order whole numbers up to 10,000; use area models to compare fractions.

Strand: OPERATIONS AND COMPUTATION

Content	Kindergarten	First Grade	Second Grade
Program Goal: Compute accurately.			
Addition and subtraction facts		**Goal 1.** Demonstrate proficiency with +/– 0, +/– 1, doubles, and sum-equals-ten addition and subtraction facts such as 6+4=10 and 10–7=3.	**Goal 1.** Demonstrate automaticity with +/– 0, +/– 1, doubles, and sum-equals-ten facts, and proficiency with all addition and subtraction facts through 10+10.
Addition and subtraction procedures	**Goal 1.** Use manipulatives, number lines, and mental arithmetic to solve problems involving the addition and subtraction of single-digit whole numbers.	**Goal 2.** Use manipulatives, number grids, tally marks, mental arithmetic, and calculators to solve problems involving the addition and subtraction of 1-digit whole numbers with 1- or 2-digit whole numbers; calculate and compare the values of combinations of coins.	**Goal 2.** Use manipulatives, number grids, tally marks, mental arithmetic, paper and pencil, and calculators to solve problems involving the addition and subtraction of 2-digit whole numbers; describe the strategies used; calculate and compare values of coin and bill combinations.
Program Goal: Make reasonable estimates.			
Computational estimation		**Goal 3.** Estimate reasonableness of answers to basic fact problems (e.g., Will 7 + 8 be more or less than 10?).	**Goal 3.** Make reasonable estimates for whole number addition and subtraction problems; explain how the estimates were obtained.
Program Goal: Understand meanings of operations.			
Models for the operations	**Goal 2.** Identify join and take-away situations.	**Goal 4.** Identify change to more, change-to-less, comparison, and parts-and-total situations.	**Goal 4.** Identify and describe change, comparison, and parts-and-total situations; use repeated addition, arrays, and skip counting to model multiplication; use equal sharing and equal grouping to model division.

Strand: DATA AND CHANCE

Content	Kindergarten	First Grade	Second Grade
Program Goal: Select and create appropriate graphical representations of collected or given data.			
Data collection and representation	**Goal 1.** Collect and organize data to create class-constructed tally charts, tables, and bar graphs.	**Goal 1.** Collect and organize data to create tally charts, tables, bar graphs, and line plots.	**Goal 1.** Collect and organize data or use given data to create tally charts, tables, bar graphs, and line plots.
Program Goal: Analyze and interpret data.			
Data analysis	**Goal 2.** Use graphs to answer simple questions.	**Goal 2.** Use graphs to answer simple questions and draw conclusions; find the maximum and minimum of a data set.	**Goal 2.** Use graphs to ask and answer simple questions and draw conclusions; find the maximum, minimum, mode, and median of a data set.
Program Goal: Understand and apply basic concepts of probability.			
Qualitative probability	**Goal 3.** Describe events using *certain, possible, impossible*, and other basic probability terms.	**Goal 3.** Describe events using *certain, likely, unlikely, impossible* and other basic probability terms.	**Goal 3.** Describe events using *certain, likely, unlikely, impossible* and other basic probability terms; explain the choice of language.

Strand: MEASUREMENT AND REFERENCE FRAMES

Content	Kindergarten	First Grade	Second Grade
Program Goal: Understand the systems and processes of measurement; use appropriate techniques, tools, units, and formulas in making measurements.			
Length, weight, and angles	**Goal 1.** Use nonstandard tools and techniques to estimate and compare weight and length; identify standard measuring tools.	**Goal 1.** Use nonstandard tools and techniques to estimate and compare weight and length; measure length with standard measuring tools.	**Goal 1.** Estimate length with and without tools; measure length to the nearest inch and centimeter; use standard and nonstandard tools to measure and estimate weight.
Area, perimeter, volume, and capacity			**Goal 2.** Count unit squares to find the area of rectangles.
Units and systems of measurement			**Goal 3.** Describe relationships between days in a week and hours in a day.
Money	**Goal 2.** Identify pennies, nickels, dimes, quarters, and dollar bills.	**Goal 2.** Know and compare the value of pennies, nickels, dimes, quarters, and dollar bills; make exchanges between coins.	**Goal 4.** Make exchanges between coins and bills.
Program Goal: Use and understand reference frames.			
Temperature	**Goal 3.** Describe temperature using appropriate vocabulary, such as *hot, warm,* and *cold;* identify a thermometer as a tool for measuring temperature.	**Goal 3.** Identify a thermometer as a tool for measuring temperature; read temperatures on Fahrenheit and Celsius thermometers to the nearest 10°.	**Goal 5.** Read temperature on both the Fahrenheit and Celsius scales.
Time	**Goal 4.** Describe and use measures of time periods relative to a day and week; identify tools that measure time.	**Goal 4.** Use a calendar to identify days, weeks, months, and dates; tell and show time to the nearest half and quarter hour on an analog clock.	**Goal 6.** Tell and show time to the nearest five minutes on an analog clock; tell and write time in digital notation.

Strand: GEOMETRY

Content	Kindergarten	First Grade	Second Grade
Program Goal: Investigate characteristics and properties of two- and three-dimensional geometric shapes.			
Lines and angles			**Goal 1.** Draw line segments and identify parallel line segments.
Plane and solid figures	**Goal 1.** Identify and describe plane and solid figures including circles, triangles, squares, rectangles, spheres, and cubes.	**Goal 1.** Identify and describe plane and solid figures including circles, triangles, squares, rectangles, spheres, cylinders, rectangular prisms, pyramids, cones, and cubes.	**Goal 2.** Identify, describe, and model plane and solid figures including circles, triangles, squares, rectangles, hexagons, trapezoids, rhombuses, spheres, cylinders, rectangular prisms, pyramids, cones, and cubes.
Program Goal: Apply transformations and symmetry in geometric situations.			
Transformations and symmetry	**Goal 2.** Identify shapes having line symmetry.	**Goal 2.** Identify shapes having line symmetry; complete line-symmetric shapes or designs.	**Goal 3.** Create and complete two-dimensional symmetric shapes or designs.

Strand: PATTERNS, FUNCTIONS, AND ALGEBRA

Content	Kindergarten	First Grade	Second Grade
Program Goal: Understand patterns and functions.			
Patterns and functions	**Goal 1.** Extend, describe, and create visual, rhythmic, and movement patterns; use rules, which will lead to functions, to sort, make patterns, and play "What's My Rule?" and other games.	**Goal 1.** Extend, describe, and create numeric, visual, and concrete patterns; solve problems involving function machines, "What's My Rule?" tables, and Frames-and-Arrows diagrams.	**Goal 1.** Extend, describe, and create numeric, visual, and concrete patterns; describe rules for patterns and use them to solve problems; use words and symbols to describe and write rules for functions involving addition and subtraction and use those rules to solve problems.
Program Goal: Use algebraic notation to represent and analyze situations and structures.			
Algebraic notation and solving number sentences	**Goal 2.** Read and write expressions and number sentences using the symbols $+$, $-$, and $=$.	**Goal 2.** Read, write, and explain expressions and number sentences using the symbols $+$, $-$, and $=$ and the symbols $>$ and $<$ with cues; solve equations involving addition and subtraction.	**Goal 2.** Read, write, and explain expressions and number sentences using the symbols $+$, $-$, $=$, $>$, and $<$; solve number sentences involving addition and subtraction; write expressions and number sentences to model number stories.
Properties of arithmetic operations		**Goal 3.** Apply the Commutative Property of Addition and the Additive Identity to basic addition fact problems.	**Goal 3.** Describe the Commutative and Associative Properties of Addition and apply them to mental arithmetic problems.

Kindergarten Assessment Opportunities

This section of the handbook is intended to help you use ongoing and periodic assessments throughout the year to provide a complete picture of children's progress toward each Kindergarten Goal.

This section is organized as follows:

Key Steps in Assessment throughout the Year

1. **Do the Baseline Periodic Assessments during the first few weeks of school.** Simply record what children know and can do. Each Baseline task appears in ongoing assessments throughout the program and in the Mid-Year and/or End-of-Year periodic assessments, often with increased difficulty.

2. **Do the activities in Sections 1–4 and use Ongoing Assessment to monitor children's progress toward Kindergarten Goals.** The ongoing assessment notes, as well as other kid-watching opportunities in these sections, will help you gather assessment information about progress toward many Kindergarten Goals. Ongoing Daily Routines are an excellent source of ongoing assessment information. There will also be Mid-Year and End-of-Year periodic assessment tasks to provide further information.

3. **Do the Mid-Year Periodic Assessments at the end of Section 4 and during Section 5.** Conducting the assessment tasks may take several weeks.

4. **Do the activities in Sections 5–8.** The ongoing assessment notes, as well as other kid-watching opportunities in these sections, will help you gather assessment information about progress toward many Kindergarten Goals. Remember that the Ongoing Daily Routines are an excellent source of ongoing assessment information.

5. **Do the End-of-Year Periodic Assessments during Section 8.** Conducting the assessment tasks may take several weeks.

Baseline, Mid-Year, and End-of-Year Periodic Assessment Tasks

Periodic assessment activities are scheduled at regular intervals during the school year to help teachers add to the assessment picture that is generated from ongoing assessment activities. While periodic assessments for older children are usually independent of normal classroom activities and often focus on paper-and-pencil assessment tasks, periodic assessment suggestions for *Kindergarten Everyday Mathematics* tend to focus on low-key interactions with the teacher and hands-on tasks, such as working with manipulatives or playing games. Many of these periodic assessment tasks are best done with individual children or in small groups, but some can be integrated as part of whole-group classroom activities.

In Kindergarten, conducting Baseline Assessment tasks during the first few weeks of the school year helps you:

◆ know your children's levels of skill and understanding, and
◆ plan instruction accordingly.

See pages 40–41 for baseline assessment suggestions.

Conducting Mid-Year and End-of-Year Periodic Assessments may add useful data about children's progress toward Grade-Level Goals to your ongoing assessment information. You can use all of this information to:

◆ plan and tailor instruction,
◆ complete report cards,
◆ conduct parent conferences,
◆ communicate with next-grade teachers, and/or
◆ report on progress toward school, district, or state expectations.

See pages 42–48 for Mid-Year and End-of-Year Periodic Assessment suggestions. You can spread your periodic assessment tasks over a period of several weeks according to the details of your particular schedule.

NOTE The periodic assessment tasks are based on the progression of activities in the *Kindergarten Everyday Mathematics Teacher's Guide to Activities.* Some skills or concepts are on multiple lists (Mid-Year and End-of-Year, for example). A few are not listed on any of the lists because they don't lend themselves to periodic assessment and are best assessed through ongoing assessment (for example, collecting and organizing data on charts and graphs). Choose (or modify) periodic assessment tasks from the lists on pages 40–48 according to your particular assessment needs. If you have already gathered adequate information about a particular skill or concept from ongoing assessment, you may not need to conduct periodic assessments on those topics for particular children or for the whole class.

Individualizing Periodic Assessment Suggestions

The periodic assessment suggestions in this section are intended to help you learn as much as possible about what individual children understand and can do at a particular point in time. To maximize the information you can learn, you will need to modify or adapt the suggestions according to the child or group of children you are working with at that moment. For example:

◆ If a child has difficulty with a task, simplify it slightly or engage the child in non-threatening conversation about the task to better understand the root of the difficulty.

◆ If they perform an activity with ease, add a bit of challenge to see how much farther they can go.

◆ Allow children to take the open-ended tasks as far as they are able. Provide encouragement for children to try things, even if they think they are difficult.

◆ If they seem perplexed by a question or set of instructions, try presenting the information in a different way to see if it makes more sense to them. Children with special needs or learning differences may require specific modifications to help them best express what they know.

In all cases, keep in mind that the periodic assessment tasks are designed to be implemented flexibly, rather than administered verbatim.

NOTE Using an approach that goes beyond simply checking whether or not a child "gets it" may require a bit more time and energy on your part. However, it will pay off in the increased information you will gather to help you tailor your instruction and communicate with parents or other teachers. You may find that this approach allows the assessment opportunities to become rich interactions for teaching and learning as well.

Tips for Implementing Periodic Assessment Tasks

Once you decide which periodic assessment tasks you will use, consider how you will administer them, keeping in mind they can be spread over a period of days or weeks. Some work best with individuals, some lend themselves well to a small group experience, and others can be integrated into ongoing classroom activities. Some of the activities can be set up in a Center where you can work with children.

Consider the options and decide what will work best for your situation. If you plan to do several one-on-one tasks with individual children or small-group assessments, you may want to cluster those tasks together in a single sitting. For tasks that you plan to do with individuals or small groups . . .

◆ Find a place where you and the children can hear each other easily and where children can concentrate.
◆ Collect and organize all needed materials beforehand.
◆ Arrange for parents or other adults to help in the classroom so you can devote your attention to the assessment activities.
◆ Set a playful tone, rather than a pressured one. You might explain to children that everyone will have a turn to play Math games with you over the course of several days (or longer).

You can use Individual Profile of Progress sheets to record information about each child's performance on the Baseline, Mid-Year, and End-of-Year periodic assessment tasks. In addition to space for specific information about children's responses to the various tasks, these sheets have space to record notes, such as children's strategies, the exact language of some of their responses, or areas where they had particular difficulty or confusion. These records are useful for communicating with parents at conference time or on report cards. See pages 85, 87–88, and 91–94 for the periodic assessment task Individual Profile of Progress sheets.

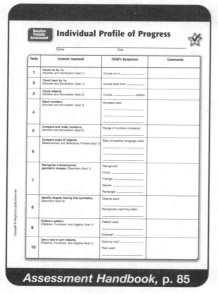

Assessment Handbook, p. 85

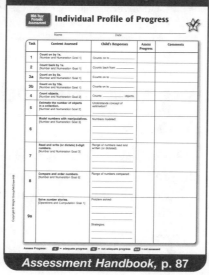

Assessment Handbook, p. 87

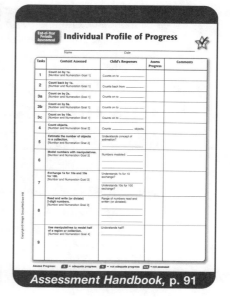

Assessment Handbook, p. 91

Later, you might transfer the periodic assessment information to a Cumulative Individual Profile of Progress for each child. The Cumulative Individual Profile of Progress sheets have space for periodic and ongoing assessment information. See pages 97–98 for a Cumulative Individual Profile of Progress to accompany Sections 1–4 of the *Teacher's Guide to Activities*. See pages 99–102 for a Cumulative Individual Profile of Progress for Sections 5–8 of the *Teacher's Guide to Activities*.

Alternatively, you can compile class results from periodic assessment tasks onto a Class Checklist. See pages 86, 89–90, and 95–96 for Class Checklists for Baseline, Mid-Year, and End-of-Year periodic assessment tasks.

Assessment Handbook, p. 86

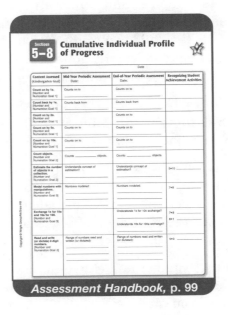

Assessment Handbook, p. 99

Periodic Assessment Tasks

Suggestions for Baseline Periodic Assessment Tasks

(Activities may be done over several days.)

1. Count on by 1s. [Number and Numeration Goal 1] Ask children to count aloud to 10. Then ask them if they can go any higher. Encourage them to count as high as they can. If a child can count very high, stop and start him or her at various numbers to more efficiently get a sense of how high he or she can count. Look for the point at which the child's counting becomes erratic.

2. Count back by 1s. [Number and Numeration Goal 1] Ask children to count backward from 5 down to 0. If a child can go backward from 5, have him or her start from 10. Note what number the child can count backward from.

3. Count objects. [Number and Numeration Goal 2] Have children count objects such as boys, girls, chairs, balls, crackers, and so on. Embed this task into ongoing classroom experiences by taking advantage of natural counting opportunities, such as setting the table or cleaning up. Look for whether the child can count up to 5, 10, 20, or more objects.

4. Read numbers. [Number and Numeration Goal 3] Give children a plastic bag containing number cards 0–5. Tell them to reach in, find, and then hold up the number you name. (You might say "1, 2, 3, show me!" to set a playful tone and ensure that everyone pulls out their cards at the same time.) Add number cards 6–10 (or beyond) to each bag for children who are ready. Group children of similar abilities together or work with individuals. Look for whether the child can read numerals 0–5, 6–10, or teens or higher.

5. Compare and order numbers. [Number and Numeration Goal 6] Show children two number cards with numbers from 0–5, and ask them to show you the higher number. Add cards through 10 if children seem ready. Look for whether the child can correctly identify the higher number and if he or she uses a reference tool to help compare the numbers.

6. Compare sizes of objects. [Measurement and Reference Frames Goal 1] Ask children to find the "smallest chair in the room" or "a chair bigger (larger) than this one." Note that early in Kindergarten, many children may be more familiar with comparisons using the terms *big, (big, bigger, biggest)* and *little* than with comparisons using *small* and *large*. Consciously use all these terms. Or use a group of toys of varying sizes and ask children to point to the one that is *"largest...," "smaller (littler)* than this ball," and so on. Look for whether the child correctly identifies objects using size comparison language.

7. Recognize two-dimensional geometric shapes. [Geometry Goal 1] Provide plastic bags containing shape cutouts or attribute block shapes, with two each of circles, triangles, and squares. Have children retrieve the shape you dictate using the "1, 2, 3, show me!" procedure. Alternatively, station yourself at a Center or at the side of the room during a playtime or Center time and call children individually to pick out shapes you name. Note whether the child correctly shows the circle, triangle, and square.

8. Identify shapes having line symmetry. [Geometry Goal 2] Show children a drawing of something symmetrical (such as a symmetrical flower or butterfly) with a vertical line of symmetry drawn on it. Ask if the two sides match. Repeat with a drawing of something that is not symmetrical (also with a line drawn through the middle). Allow children to manipulate the drawing (by touching, folding, and so on) if desired. If children correctly identify left and right matching sides, you might show a symmetrical drawing with a horizontal line of symmetry and top and bottom halves matching, such as a ball with symmetrical markings. Look for whether the child can determine if two sides of an object or drawing match one another.

9. Extend a pattern. [Patterns, Functions, and Algebra Goal 1] Begin a simple movement pattern (clap, snap; clap, snap; clap, snap; and so on) or a color pattern with connecting cubes. Invite children to extend your pattern, and observe what they do. For children who are proficient, you might repeat with a more complicated pattern (for example, clap, clap, snap; clap, clap, snap;...) and see if they can extend it. Note whether the child can correctly extend the pattern you began.

10. Use a rule to sort objects. [Patterns, Functions, and Algebra Goal 1] Give children a bag of objects varying in color, size, and/or shape. Tell them to sort (group) the objects, but do not specify a particular sorting rule. When the task is complete, ask children to explain how they sorted the objects (by size, color, or shape, for example). Specify a sorting criterion (color, size, and so on) and evaluate children's ability to sort according to the rule you provide. Look for whether the child is aware of the different attributes of objects and the concept of sorting.

Notes

_____

_____

_____

_____

_____

_____

_____

_____

Suggestions for Mid-Year Periodic Assessment Tasks

NOTE In addition to determining whether children are making adequate progress toward each Kindergarten goal (as described in the last sentence of each task description below), note the specific level of proficiency they demonstrate with each task.

1. Count on by 1s. [Number and Numeration Goal 1] Start with any number other than 0 or 1, and ask children to count to some specified number. Start counting again from a different number. Continue with higher numbers until the child begins to have difficulty. Allow children who are having difficulty to look at a number line or number grid for reference. Look for the child to count to at least 30 from different starting numbers.

2. Count back by 1s. [Number and Numeration Goal 1] Ask children to count back from 10 to 0. If they do this easily, give a starting number in the low teens and have them count back for a string of several numbers. Gradually increase the starting number. Encourage children to look at a number line or number grid for reference if needed. Look for the child to count back from at least 10 to 0.

3. Count on by 5s and 10s. [Number and Numeration Goal 1] Ask children to start from 0 and skip count by 10s as high as they can. Repeat, this time asking them to skip count by 5s. Children may use a number line or number grid as a reference tool. Look for the child to count on to at least 50 by 10s and by 5s.

4. Count objects. [Number and Numeration Goal 2] Present children with a collection of 10–20 objects, and ask them to count how many you have. For those who are ready, add objects to go above 20 and ask them to count again. Look for the child to count at least 20 objects.

5. Estimate the number of objects in a collection. [Number and Numeration Goal 2] Show children a jar with 10–20 objects and a reference jar with a known quantity (perhaps 10) of the same objects. Ask children to estimate how many are in the estimation jar and explain why they made their estimate. If children make wild guesses, try putting fewer objects in the jar to see whether they are able to estimate (without counting). Look for the child to make an educated, rather than a wild guess to estimate items in a collection, and to explain his or her reasoning.

6. Model numbers with manipulatives. [Number and Numeration Goal 3] Provide straws or craft sticks and rubber bands and ask children to use the materials to represent a number that you name. Begin with a number less than 10. Then try a teen number. Repeat for higher numbers with children who seem ready (those who are bundling sticks and thinking about tens and ones). Look for the child to show a number with single sticks or with bundles of 10 and single sticks.

7. Read and write (or dictate) 2-digit numbers. [Number and Numeration Goal 3] Beginning with numbers in the teens, ask children to tell you how to write 2-digit numbers that you name. Repeat for a number in the 20s and one in the 30s. Then write or point to some 2-digit numbers and ask children to name the numbers. Again, begin with teens and gradually increase. If children seem ready, ask them to name or write 2-digit numbers in the 40s and higher. Look for the child to read and write (or dictate) 2-digit numbers to at least 30.

8. Compare and order numbers. [Number and Numeration Goal 6] Play a few rounds of *Top-It* with children. Begin with 0–10 cards. If children seem ready, add cards through 20. Provide a reference tool to help with comparing numbers for children who need it. Look for the child to identify the higher card for numbers 0–10 or higher in each round of *Top-It*.

9. Solve number stories. [Operations and Computation Goal 1], and **Identify join and take-away situations.** [Operations and Computation Goal 2] Pick a number story page from the middle section (Part 2) of *Minute Math*. Ask children to solve it and observe what strategies they use. Provide manipulatives, number lines, or other tools that children can use to solve the stories. Ask whether it is a join or take-away (addition or subtraction) story. If they seem ready, have children tell a join or take-away story. Look for the child to solve simple addition and subtraction number stories. (They may still have difficulty identifying join and take-away stories.)

10. Describe events using basic probability terms. [Data and Chance Goal 3] Put an assortment of attribute blocks on a tray. Before children pick a block from the tray, ask them questions such as: *Is it possible that you will pick a red square? Are you certain to get a blue block? Are you more likely to pick a blue block or a red block? Why?* (See Activity 3-11 for additional sample questions.) Look for the child to answer questions that are phrased in terms of basic probability terms, such as *certain, possible,* and *impossible.* (Children are not necessarily expected to use *more likely* and *less likely* yet, although many children will.)

11. Use nonstandard tools and techniques to estimate and compare weight and length. [Measurement and Reference Frames Goal 1] Show children a collection of three or more objects, at least two the same size. Ask them to arrange them in order of length. Prompt with questions such as: *Which is the longest? Are any of them the same length? How do you know?* Then ask children to arrange them in order of weight. Invite children to use tools to find out more about the length and weight of the objects. Watch which tools they choose (perhaps connecting cubes and a pan balance) and how they use the tools. For children who have difficulty working with 3 objects at a time, begin with direct comparisons of 2 objects and ask questions such as: *Which is longer? Are they the same length? Which is heavier?* Look for the child to correctly compare the length and weight of objects and to choose and use tools to measure the length and weight of objects.

12. Identify plane (2-dimensional) figures. [Geometry Goal 1] Put a collection of pattern blocks and attribute blocks on a tray. Ask children to remove the shapes you name from the tray. Begin by asking for circles, triangles, rectangles, and squares. Ask children who seem ready for additional shapes, such as hexagons. Look for the child to at least identify circles, triangles, rectangles, and squares.

13. Identify shapes having line symmetry. [Geometry Goal 2] Show children a drawing of something symmetrical, such as a butterfly with symmetrical markings. Ask: *Is it symmetrical? Why (or why not)?* Alternatively, provide several pre-cut shapes (some symmetrical; some not) and have children sort them according to whether or not they are symmetrical. Look for the child to recognize that both sides must match if an object is symmetrical.

14. Extend, describe, and create patterns. [Patterns, Functions, and Algebra Goal 1] Ask children to create a pattern with pattern blocks and to describe their patterns. If children create a 2-part pattern, continue by asking them to extend a 3-part pattern that you create. (For example: show triangle, hexagon, diamond; triangle, hexagon, diamond; …). Ask children if they can create and describe a more complicated pattern. Look for the child to create and/or extend 2- and 3-part patterns and describe the patterns.

15. Use a rule to sort objects. [Patterns, Functions, and Algebra Goal 1] Have children sort a collection of attribute blocks according to an attribute that you specify (size, shape, color, or thickness). When they complete this task, ask them to sort again using another attribute of their choice. Look for the child to sort blocks by a given attribute and by an attribute of their choice.

Notes

_____

_____

_____

_____

_____

_____

_____

_____

_____

_____

_____

_____

Suggestions for End-of-Year Periodic Assessment Tasks

NOTE In addition to determining whether children are making adequate progress toward each Kindergarten goal (as described in the last sentence of each task description below), note the specific level of proficiency they demonstrate with each task.

1. Count on by 1s. [Number and Numeration Goal 1] Start with any number other than 0 or 1 and ask children to count to some specified number. Start counting again from a different number. Continue until the child begins to have difficulty. Look for the child to count to at least 100 from various numbers.

2. Count back by 1s. [Number and Numeration Goal 1] Ask children to count back from a number in at least the teens or twenties. Invite them to use a reference tool, such as a number line or number grid, if needed. Look for the child to count back by 1s from a number beyond 10.

3. Count on by 2s, 5s and 10s. [Number and Numeration Goal 1] Ask children to start from 0 and skip count by 2s as high as they can. Repeat, this time asking them to skip count by 10s, then by 5s. Children may use a number line or number grid as a reference tool. Look for the child to count on by 2s, by 5s, and by 10s.

4. Count objects. [Number and Numeration Goal 2] Present children with a collection of 10–20 objects, and ask them to count how many you have. For those who are ready, add more objects. Look for the child to count at least 20 objects in a collection.

5. Estimate the number of objects in a collection. [Number and Numeration Goal 2] Show children a jar with 10–20 objects and a reference jar with a known quantity (perhaps 10) of the same objects. Ask children to estimate how many are in the estimation jar and explain why they made their estimate. For children who are ready, use more than 20 objects in the estimate jar. Look for the child to make an educated, rather than a wild guess to estimate items in a collection, and to explain his or her reasoning.

6. Model numbers with manipulatives. [Number and Numeration Goal 3] Provide single straws or craft sticks, as well as some bundles of 10. Ask children to use the materials to represent numbers that you name. Begin with a teen number and see if they use a bundle of 10 and single sticks. (Some children may count out the number of single sticks without using a bundle of 10. Ask these children if they can make the number using a bundle.) Repeat for higher numbers with children who can easily do teen numbers. Include a big bundle of 100 sticks or straws and ask for a number in the 100s for children who are ready. Look for the child to show a teen or higher number using bundles of 10 sticks and one or more single sticks.

7. Exchange 1s for 10s and 10s for 100. [Number and Numeration Goal 3] Provide rubber bands and a large number of craft sticks (at least 30; not an even 10). Invite children to make bundles of 10 or exchanges with pre-bundled sticks. Have them count the total by 10s and 1s. Next, show 10 bundles of 10 craft sticks and ask children what they could trade it for. Look for the child to exchange 1s for 10s and 10s for 100.

8. Read and write (or dictate) 2-digit numbers. [Number and Numeration Goal 3] Ask children to tell you how to write 2-digit numbers that you name. Then write or point to some 2-digit numbers and ask children to name the numbers. Start with numbers below 30, then increase. For children who are ready, move to writing and reading 3-digit numbers. Look for the child to read and write (or dictate) 2-digit numbers through at least 30.

9. Use manipulatives to model half of a region or collection. [Number and Numeration Goal 4] Give children a cracker or picture of a cracker. Have them divide it in half. Also give an even-numbered collection of items for children to divide in half. Ask children to explain why what they've made are called *halves*. Look for the child to model and describe half of a region or collection and to understand that the two halves should be the same size.

10. Give equivalent names for numbers. [Number and Numeration Goal 5] Ask children to create a name collection for the number 15. (Use a lower number if 15 seems too high for some.) Probe to expand the different types of representations they include, as needed. If children are ready, ask them to create a name collection for a number in the 20s. Look for the child to use manipulatives, drawings, and numerical expressions involving addition and subtraction of 1-digit numbers to give equivalent names for numbers up to at least 20. Note whether they understand that numbers can be represented in different ways.

11. Compare and order numbers. [Number and Numeration Goal 6] Play *Top-It* with children. Use 0–20 cards. After the game, select three cards and ask children to order them from smallest to largest. Look for the child to compare and order numbers up to at least 20.

12. Solve number stories. [Operations and Computation Goal 1], **Identify join and take-away situations.** [Operations and Computation Goal 2], and **Read and write expressions and number sentences using the symbols +, −, and =.** [Patterns, Functions, and Algebra Goal 2] Pick addition and subtraction number story pages from the middle or last section of *Minute Math*. Ask children to solve the stories and observe what strategies they use. (Provide manipulatives, number lines, or other tools.) Ask whether each story is a join or take-away (addition or subtraction) story. Also have the children write a number model to match each number story or enter the problem on a calculator.

Look for the child to use manipulatives, number lines, and mental arithmetic to solve number stories and to identify join and take-away situations. Also look for the child to use +, −, and = symbols to read and write expressions and number sentences to model the stories.

13. Use graphs to answer simple questions. [Data and Chance Goal 2] Show a familiar graph (a class graph or a child's survey graph). Ask some questions about the graph. Begin with basic questions, such as: *What does this graph tell us? Which category has the most (and least)?* If the children are ready, progress to more difficult questions, such as comparing two categories. *(Which is more?)* For children who seem ready, you might ask: *How many more?* Look for the child to use graphs to answer simple questions.

14. Describe events using basic probability terms. [Data and Chance Goal 3] Put an assortment of red and blue attribute blocks on a tray. Before children pick a block from the tray, ask them questions, such as: *Is it possible that you will pick a red block? Are you certain to pick a red block? Are you more likely to pick a blue block or a red block? Why?* (See Activity 3-11 for additional sample questions.) Look for the child to describe events using *certain, possible, impossible,* and other basic probability terms.

15. Use nonstandard tools and techniques to estimate and compare weight and length. [Measurement and Reference Frames Goal 1] Set out a collection of objects and ask children: *Which is longest? How can you check? Which is heaviest? How can you check?* Watch their choices of tools and use of measuring techniques. Look for the child to use nonstandard tools and techniques to estimate and compare length and weight.

16. Identify pennies, nickels, dimes, quarters, and dollar bills. [Measurement and Reference Frames Goal 2] Show a mixed collection of money (pennies, nickels, dimes, quarters, and a dollar bill). Ask children to find each coin or bill you name. Ask whether they know the value of each. For some children, you might invite them to make some trades. *(Which coin could I trade these five pennies for? Do you want to trade anything for this dime?)* Look for the child to correctly identify a penny, nickel, dime, quarter, and dollar bill.

17. Identify standard measuring tools. [Measurement and Reference Frames Goals 1, 3, and 4] Show children a thermometer, analog clock, pan balance, and ruler (or a picture of these tools). Ask: *Which tool would you use to measure temperature? Which would you use to measure time? Length? Weight?* You might also ask children to tell you what other tools they know of to measure time, temperature, length, and weight. Look for the child to identify tools for measuring temperature, time, weight, and length.

18. Describe and use time periods relative to a day and week. [Measurement and Reference Frames Goal 4] With your class calendar and daily schedule available for reference, ask children questions such as the following:

◆ *Name something we will do this morning (or afternoon).*
◆ *What will we do after that?*
◆ *Point to today on the calendar. What day is today?*
◆ *Point to yesterday (or tomorrow). What day was yesterday (will tomorrow be)?*

Tailor the difficulty of your questions to children's level of understanding. Look for the child to use terms such as morning, afternoon, yesterday, today, tomorrow, and sequencing words to describe time periods relative to a day and week.

19. Identify 2-dimensional shapes and 3-dimensional solids. [Geometry Goal 1] Ask: *Can you find a sphere in the classroom? A cube?* Include other 3-D shapes if children are ready. Begin with 2-dimensional shapes for children who struggled with this during previous assessments. Look for the child to identify a circle, triangle, square, rectangle, sphere, and cube.

20. Identify shapes having line symmetry. [Geometry Goal 2] Show children a drawing of something symmetrical, such as a butterfly with symmetrical markings. Ask: *Is it symmetrical? Why (or why not)?* Alternatively, provide several pre-cut shapes (some symmetrical; some not) and have children sort them according to whether or not they are symmetrical. Look for the child to recognize that both sides must match if an object is symmetrical and to identify objects having line symmetry.

21. Extend, describe, and create patterns. [Patterns, Functions, and Algebra Goal 1] Ask children to create a pattern with pattern blocks and to describe it. If children create a 2-part pattern, continue by asking them to extend a 3-part pattern that you create (for example: triangle, hexagon, diamond; triangle, hexagon, diamond; ...). Ask them to extend your pattern. Ask children if they can create and describe a more complicated pattern. Look for the child to create and/or extend 2- and 3-part patterns and describe the patterns.

22. Use a rule to sort objects. [Patterns, Functions, and Algebra Goal 1] Have children sort a collection of attribute blocks according to an attribute that you specify (size, shape, color, or thickness). When they complete this task, ask them to sort again using another attribute of their choice. Look for the child to use rules to sort in different ways.

23. Use rules for *"What's My Rule?" Fishing.* [Patterns, Functions, and Algebra Goal 1] Play *"What's My Rule?" Fishing* in large or small groups. Ensure that all children get a chance to guess the rule over a period of time. Look for the child to understand the basic concept behind "What's My Rule?" activities.

Notes

_____

_____

_____

_____

_____

_____

_____

Assessment Overview by Section

The information in this section of the handbook is intended to summarize the ongoing and periodic assessment opportunities in each section of the *Teacher's Guide to Activities*.

The pages in this section are organized by section as follows:

Assessment Overview

Ongoing Assessment

Ongoing assessment involves observing children during daily activities. The four major ongoing assessment opportunities are Kid-Watching, Recognizing Student Achievement, Informing Instruction, and Portfolio Opportunities.

Be on the lookout for kid-watching opportunities as children do the Ongoing Daily Routines, the Core Activities, and the Teaching Options, as well as at various other times when they use mathematics throughout the day. (See pages 66–75 for specific kid-watching suggestions organized by mathematical strand.)

Recognizing Student Achievement

The information in this chart summarizes the Recognizing Student Achievement (RSA) opportunities that are highlighted in Section 1.

Activity	Content Assessed	Where to Find It
1◆13	**Comparing lengths of two objects** [Measurement and Reference Frames Goal 1]	Body Height Comparisons (*Teacher's Guide to Activities*, p. 71)
1◆14	**Counting up to 10 objects** [Number and Numeration Goal 2] **Recognizing numbers 1–10** [Number and Numeration Goal 3]	Showing Fingers (*Teacher's Guide to Activities*, p. 72)

Informing Instruction

The Informing Instruction opportunities highlight children's thinking and suggest ways to enhance it, as well as ways to avoid misunderstandings. Informing Instruction in Section 1 appears in the following activities: 1-1, 1-3, 1-5, 1-10, and 1-12.

Portfolio Opportunities

The information in this table summarizes the portfolio opportunities that are highlighted in Section 1.

Activity	Portfolio Opportunity	What to Look For
1♦2	Children create paper quilts by cutting shapes to arrange and glue on paper. **Collect** paper quilts. (Literacy Connection Teaching Option)	• Can the child identify the shapes he or she uses in the quilt? • Do the children incorporate patterns into their paper quilts? How do they describe the patterns?
1♦5	Children make their own pages about the featured number for the day. **Collect** number pages. (Getting to Know Numbers Core Activity)	• Does the child correctly represent the number on the page with drawings, stickers, or objects? • Can the child recognize the number on the page? • Can the child write the number without help? If not, can they write the number with help?

Periodic Assessment

Periodic assessment occurs at regular intervals during the school year. *Kindergarten Everyday Mathematics* suggests that you conduct Baseline, Mid-Year, and End-of-Year periodic assessment tasks.

◆ **During Section 1** Conduct the Baseline periodic assessment tasks during the first few weeks of school.

◆ **Looking Ahead** The next periodic assessment will be the Mid-Year Periodic Assessment (see page 42–44) which occurs after Section 4 and may continue during Section 5. The Mid-Year periodic assessment tasks include all of the content covered on the Baseline Assessment as well as some additional content. The End-of-Year Periodic Assessment will occur during Section 8.

Assessment Overview

Ongoing Assessment

Ongoing assessment involves observing children during daily activities. The four major ongoing assessment opportunities are Kid-Watching, Recognizing Student Achievement, Informing Instruction, and Portfolio Opportunities.

Be on the lookout for kid-watching opportunities as children do the Ongoing Daily Routines, the Core Activities, and the Teaching Options, as well as at various other times when they use mathematics throughout the day. (See pages 66–75 for specific kid-watching suggestions organized by mathematical strand.)

Recognizing Student Achievement

The information in this chart summarizes the Recognizing Student Achievement (RSA) opportunities that are highlighted in Section 2.

Activity	Content Assessed	Where to Find It
2✦2	**Identifying and naming a triangle and a circle** [Geometry Goal 1]	Shapes by Feel (*Teacher's Guide to Activities,* p. 90)
2✦4	**Counting up to 10 objects** [Number and Numeration Goal 2] **Reading numbers 1–10** [Number and Numeration Goal 3]	*Spin a Number* Game (*Teacher's Guide to Activities,* p. 95)
2✦16	**Identifying symmetrical objects** [Geometry Goal 2]	Symmetry in Nature (*Teacher's Guide to Activities,* p. 123)

Informing Instruction

The Informing Instruction (II) opportunities highlight children's thinking and suggest ways to enhance it, as well as ways to avoid misunderstandings. Informing Instruction in Section 2 appears in the following activities: 2-1, 2-6, 2-7, 2-11, and 2-14.

Portfolio Opportunities

The information in this table summarizes the Portfolio Opportunities that are highlighted in Section 2.

Activity	Portfolio Opportunity	What to Look For
2◆2	Children use shapes to create art projects. **Collect** shape art projects. (Art Connection Teaching Option)	• Can the child identify the shapes he or she uses in the project?
2◆11	Children construct buildings using an identified (teen) number of blocks. **Collect** photographs of children's teen buildings. (Mathematics in the Block Center Teaching Option)	• Can the child correctly count the number of blocks on his or her building? • Can the child compare the size of his or her buildings with other children's teen buildings?
2◆14	Children use drawing and writing to tell and solve number stories. **Collect** children's number story drawings. (Mathematics in the Writing Center Teaching Option)	• Can the child represent a number story with pictures (and perhaps some words)? • Can the child use drawings to help solve number stories?

Periodic Assessment

Periodic assessment occurs at regular intervals during the school year. *Kindergarten Everyday Mathematics* suggests that you conduct Baseline, Mid-Year, and End-of-Year periodic assessment tasks.

◆ **During Section 2** Be sure you have completed the Baseline periodic assessment tasks.

◆ **Looking Ahead** The next periodic assessment will be the Mid-Year Periodic Assessment (see pages 42–44) which occurs after Section 4 and may continue during Section 5. The Mid-Year periodic assessment tasks include all of the content covered on the Baseline Assessment as well as some additional content. The End-of-Year Periodic Assessment will occur during Section 8.

Ongoing Assessment

Ongoing assessment involves observing children during daily activities. The four major ongoing assessment opportunities are Kid-Watching, Recognizing Student Achievement, Informing Instruction, and Portfolio Opportunities.

Be on the lookout for kid-watching opportunities as children do the Ongoing Daily Routines, the Core Activities, and the Teaching Options, as well as at various other times when they use mathematics throughout the day. (See pages 66–75 for specific kid-watching suggestions organized by mathematical strand.)

Recognizing Student Achievement

The information in this chart summarizes the Recognizing Student Achievement (RSA) opportunities that are highlighted in Section 3.

Activity	Content Assessed	Where to Find It
3◆1	**Drawing correct quantities of items to represent numbers** [Number and Numeration Goal 2]	Number Books (*Teacher's Guide to Activities,* p. 139)
3◆2	**Creating, describing, and extending patterns** [Patterns, Functions, and Algebra Goal 1]	Macaroni Necklaces (*Teacher's Guide to Activities,* p. 140)
3◆5	**Counting 1–12 objects** [Number and Numeration Goal 2] **Recognizing numbers** [Number and Numeration Goal 3]	*Domino Concentration* Game (*Teacher's Guide to Activities,* p. 149)
3◆16	**Counting numbers 11–20** [Number and Numeration Goal 2] **Comparing numbers 11–20** [Number and Numeration Goal 6]	*Teen Frame* Game (*Teacher's Guide to Activities,* p. 173)

Informing Instruction

The Informing Instruction (II) opportunities highlight children's thinking and suggest ways to enhance it as well as ways to avoid misunderstandings. Informing Instruction in Section 3 appears in the following activities: 3-6, 3-9, 3-11, 3-12, 3-13, and 3-14.

Portfolio Opportunities

The information in this table summarizes the Portfolio Opportunities that are highlighted in Section 3.

Activity	Portfolio Opportunity	What to Look For
3◆1	**Children use writing and drawing to create number books.** **Collect** number book pages. (Writing Numbers 0–10 Core Activity)	• Can the child draw the correct number of objects for each numeral? • Is the child comfortable writing numerals?
3◆2	**Children create patterned macaroni necklaces.** **Collect** photographs of necklaces. (Making Macaroni Necklaces Core Activity)	• What type of pattern does the child create? • How does the child describe his or her pattern?
3◆4	**Children use drawing and writing to create pan-balance records.** **Collect** pan-balance records. (Introducing the Pan Balance Core Activity)	• Does the child show the relative positions of each arm on the pan-balance? Does he or she understand what the positions indicate (heavier/lighter)?
3◆7	**Children use drawing and writing to record measurements.** **Collect** measurement records. (Measuring with Nonstandard Units Core Activity)	• Does the child's record accurately depict measurements? Does it include units? • Does the child use drawing, numbers, and/or writing to record measurements?
3◆8	**Children create dice roll graphs or play** *Dice Race.* **Collect** Roll and Record Sheets. (Graphing Dice Rolls Revisit Activity)	• Is the child able to navigate and complete the grid? • Does the child use shading or write numbers on the grid? • Can the child answer questions about his or her completed grid?

Periodic Assessment

Periodic assessment occurs at regular intervals during the school year. *Kindergarten Everyday Mathematics* suggests that you conduct Baseline, Mid-Year, and End-of-Year periodic assessment tasks.

◆ **During Section 3** There are no periodic assessment tasks to conduct during Section 3.

◆ **Looking Ahead** The next periodic assessment will be the Mid-Year Periodic Assessment (see pages 42–44) which occurs after Section 4 and may continue during Section 5. The Mid-Year periodic assessment tasks include all of the content covered on the Baseline Assessment as well as some additional content. The End-of-Year Periodic Assessment will occur during Section 8.

Assessment Overview

Ongoing Assessment

Ongoing assessment involves observing children during daily activities. The four major ongoing assessment opportunities are Kid-Watching, Recognizing Student Achievement, Informing Instruction, and Portfolio Opportunities.

Be on the lookout for kid-watching opportunities as children do the Ongoing Daily Routines, the Core Activities, and the Teaching Options, as well as at various other times when they use mathematics throughout the day. (See pages 66–75 for specific kid-watching suggestions organized by mathematical strand.)

Recognizing Student Achievement

The information in this chart summarizes the Recognizing Student Achievement (RSA) opportunities that are highlighted in Section 4.

Activity	Content Assessed	Where to Find It
4✦2	**Comparing numbers 0–20** [Number and Numeration Goal 6]	*Top-It* Game (*Teacher's Guide to Activities*, p. 191)
4✦5	**Creating, extending, and describing patterns** [Patterns, Functions, and Algebra Goal 1]	Follow My Pattern (*Teacher's Guide to Activities*, p. 197)
4✦6	**Counting by 1s through 30** [Number and Numeration Goal 1] **Counting backward** [Number and Numeration Goal 1]	Interrupted Counts (*Teacher's Guide to Activities*, p. 199)
4✦13	**Recognizing and naming basic shapes** [Geometry Goal 1] **Sorting according to color, shape, or size** [Patterns, Functions, and Algebra Goal 1]	Attribute Blocks (*Teacher's Guide to Activities*, p. 214)

Informing Instruction

The Informing Instruction (II) opportunities highlight children's thinking and suggest ways to enhance it, as well as ways to avoid misunderstandings. Informing Instruction in Section 4 appears in the following activities: 4-7, 4-10, 4-12, and 4-16.

Portfolio Opportunities

The information in this table summarizes the Portfolio Opportunities that are highlighted in Section 4.

Activity	Portfolio Opportunity	What to Look For
4♦3, 4♦4	**Children use pattern-block templates to create pattern strips.** **Collect** pattern strips. (Exploring the Pattern-Block Template Core Activity; Creating Pattern Strips Revisit Activity)	• What type of pattern does the child create and represent? • Is the child able to use the pattern-block template?
4♦8	**Children use shading or writing to create Dice-Throw Grids.** **Collect** Dice-Throw Grids. (Graphing Sums of Dice Core Activity)	• Is the child able to navigate and complete the grid? • Does the child use shading or write numbers on his or her grid? • Can the child answer questions about his or her completed grid?

Periodic Assessment

Periodic assessment occurs at regular intervals during the school year. *Kindergarten Everyday Mathematics* suggests that you conduct Baseline, Mid-Year, and End-of-Year periodic assessment tasks.

◆ **During Section 4** Plan to conduct the Mid-Year Periodic Assessment after completing Section 4. (You can start toward the end of the section, if desired.) Continue conducting the Mid-Year periodic assessment tasks as you begin Section 5.

◆ **Looking Ahead** The next periodic assessment will be the End-of-Year Periodic Assessment (see pages 45–48), which occurs during Section 8. The End-of-Year periodic assessment tasks include all of the content covered on the Mid-Year Assessment as well as some additional content.

Assessment Overview

Ongoing Assessment

Ongoing assessment involves observing children during daily activities. The four major ongoing assessment opportunities are Kid-Watching, Recognizing Student Achievement, Informing Instruction, and Portfolio Opportunities.

Be on the lookout for kid-watching opportunities as children do the Ongoing Daily Routines, the Core Activities, and the Teaching Options, as well as at various other times when they use mathematics throughout the day. (See pages 66–75 for specific kid-watching suggestions organized by mathematical strand.)

Recognizing Student Achievement

The information in this chart summarizes the Recognizing Student Achievement (RSA) opportunities that are highlighted in Section 5.

Activity	Content Assessed	Where to Find It
5✦1	**Sequencing events and describing time periods of the day** [Measurement and Reference Frames Goal 4]	Order of Daily Events (*Teacher's Guide to Activities*, p. 237)
5✦3	**Reading and writing 2-digit numbers** [Number and Numeration Goal 3]	Slate activities (*Teacher's Guide to Activities*, p. 241)
5✦10	**Making reasonable estimates** [Number and Numeration Goal 2]	Estimating Beans (*Teacher's Guide to Activities*, p. 255)
5✦13	**Answering questions based on a graph** [Data and Chance Goal 2]	Graphing Pets (*Teacher's Guide to Activities*, p. 261)

Informing Instruction

The Informing Instruction (II) opportunities highlight children's thinking and suggest ways to enhance it, as well as ways to avoid misunderstandings. Informing Instruction in Section 5 appears in the following activities: 5-4, 5-11, 5-14, and 5-15.

Portfolio Opportunities

The information in this table summarizes the Portfolio Opportunities that are highlighted in Section 5.

Activity	Portfolio Opportunity	What to Look For
5◆1	**Children create daily event timelines.** **Collect** timelines. (Sequencing Daily Events Core Activity)	• Does the child sequence events correctly on his or her timeline? • How does the child describe the time of day for each event?

Periodic Assessment

Periodic assessment occurs at regular intervals during the school year. *Kindergarten Everyday Mathematics* suggests that you conduct Baseline, Mid-Year, and End-of-Year periodic assessment tasks.

◆ **During Section 5** If you haven't already completed it, plan to finish the Mid-Year Periodic Assessment during Section 5.

◆ **Looking Ahead** The next periodic assessment will be the End-of-Year Periodic Assessment (see pages 45–48), which occurs during Section 8. The End-of-Year periodic assessment tasks include all of the content covered on the Mid-Year Assessment as well as some additional content.

Assessment Overview

Ongoing Assessment

Ongoing assessment involves observing children during daily activities. The four major ongoing assessment opportunities are Kid-Watching, Recognizing Student Achievement, Informing Instruction, and Portfolio Opportunities.

Be on the lookout for kid-watching opportunities as children do the Ongoing Daily Routines, the Core Activities, and the Teaching Options, as well as at various other times when they use mathematics throughout the day. (See pages 66–75 for specific kid-watching suggestions organized by mathematical strand.)

Recognizing Student Achievement

The information in this chart summarizes the Recognizing Student Achievement (RSA) opportunities that are highlighted in Section 6.

Activity	Content Assessed	Where to Find It
6◆7	**Counting by 10s** [Number and Numeration Goal 1]	Exploring the Dime (*Teacher's Guide to Activities*, p. 297)
6◆8	**Identifying pennies, nickels, and dimes** [Measurement and Reference Frames Goal 2]	Coin Exchanges (*Teacher's Guide to Activities*, p. 298)
6◆9	**Using nonstandard measuring tools and units to measure length** [Measurement and Reference Frames Goal 1]	Measuring in Different Ways (*Teacher's Guide to Activities*, p. 301)
6◆12	**Using attribute rules to find objects** [Patterns, Functions, and Algebra Goal 1]	*Read My Mind* Game (Teacher's Guide to Activities, p. 307)
6◆15	**Using basic probability terms** [Data and Chance Goal 3]	Flipping a Coin (*Teacher's Guide to Activities*, p. 313)

Informing Instruction

The Informing Instruction (II) opportunities highlight children's thinking and suggest ways to enhance it as well as ways to avoid misunderstandings. Informing Instruction in Section 6 appears in the following activities: 6-6 and 6-16.

Portfolio Opportunities

The information in this table summarizes the Portfolio Opportunities that are highlighted in Section 6.

Activity	Portfolio Opportunity	What to Look For
6◆5	**Children create survey lists and graphs.** **Collect** graphs. (Graphing Survey Data Core Activity)	• Can the child collect and record survey data? • Can the child represent the data on a graph? • Can the child interpret his or her survey graph?
6◆12	**Children use various materials to create attribute collages.** **Collect** art collages. (Art Connection Teaching Option)	• Does the child focus on a single attribute in his or her collage?

Periodic Assessment

Periodic assessment occurs at regular intervals during the school year. *Kindergarten Everyday Mathematics* suggests that you conduct Baseline, Mid-Year, and End-of-Year periodic assessment tasks.

◆ **During Section 6** There are no periodic assessment tasks to conduct during Section 6.

◆ **Looking Ahead** The next periodic assessment will be the End-of-Year Periodic Assessment (see pages 45–48), which occurs during Section 8. The End-of-Year periodic assessment tasks include all of the content covered on the Mid-Year Assessment as well as some additional content.

Assessment Overview

Ongoing Assessment

Ongoing assessment involves observing children during daily activities. The four major ongoing assessment opportunities are Kid-Watching, Recognizing Student Achievement, Informing Instruction, and Portfolio Opportunities.

Be on the lookout for kid-watching opportunities as children do the Ongoing Daily Routines, the Core Activities, and the Teaching Options, as well as at various other times when they use mathematics throughout the day. (See pages 66–75 for specific kid-watching suggestions organized by mathematical strand.)

Recognizing Student Achievement

The information in this chart summarizes the Recognizing Student Achievement (RSA) opportunities that are highlighted in Section 7.

Activity	Content Assessed	Where to Find It
7◆1	**Identifying names and values of coins** [Measurement and Reference Frames Goal 2]	*Money Cube* Game (Teacher's Guide to Activities, p. 331)
7◆3	**Identifying addition and subtraction stories** [Operations and Computation Goal 2] **Using +, −, and = symbols to represent number stories** [Patterns, Functions, and Algebra Goal 2]	Creating Number Stories (*Teacher's Guide to Activities*, p. 337)
7◆4	**Modeling half of a collection** [Number and Numeration Goal 4]	Dividing Groups in Half (*Teacher's Guide to Activities*, p. 341)
7◆6	**Adding small numbers** [Operations and Computation Goal 1]	*Dice Addition* Games (*Teacher's Guide to Activities*, p. 345)
7◆8	**Using manipulatives to model numbers and make exchanges** [Number and Numeration Goal 3]	Bundling Sticks (*Teacher's Guide to Activities*, p. 349)
7◆14	**Comparing and ordering numbers** [Number and Numeration Goal 6]	Ordering Numbers (*Teacher's Guide to Activities*, p. 360)

Informing Instruction

The Informing Instruction (II) opportunities highlight children's thinking and suggest ways to enhance it, as well as ways to avoid misunderstandings. Informing Instruction in Section 7 appears in the following activities: 7-2, 7-7, and 7-10.

Portfolio Opportunities

The information in this table summarizes the Portfolio Opportunities that are highlighted in Section 7.

Activity	Portfolio Opportunity	What to Look For
7•3, 7•6	Children create Number Story pages. **Collect** Number Story pages. (Creating Number Stories Core Activity)	• Can the child represent his or her number story with pictures? • Can the child represent his or her number story with a number sentence?
7•4	Children create 2- or 3-dimensional marshmallow and toothpick structures. **Collect** photographs of children's structures. (Making Geometric Shapes with Marshmallows and Toothpicks Core Activity)	• What types of shapes does the child create? • Can the child describe or name shapes in his or her structures?
7•9	Children create connecting cube representations of equivalent numbers; children use writing and drawing to record their combinations. **Collect** drawings or photographs of children's representations. (Representing Numbers with Connecting Cubes Teaching Option)	• Can the child use different combinations of connecting cubes to represent numbers? • Does the child use 2 different colors or more than 2 colors to represent numbers with cubes?
7•10	Children create number scrolls. **Collect** number scrolls. (Making Number Scrolls Core Activity)	• What is the highest number on the child's scroll? • Does the child write the numbers correctly and in the correct positions? • Does the child use knowledge of number patterns when filling in his or her scroll?

Periodic Assessment

Periodic assessment occurs at regular intervals during the school year. *Kindergarten Everyday Mathematics* suggests that you conduct Baseline, Mid-Year, and End-of-Year periodic assessment tasks.

◆ **During Section 7** There are no periodic assessment tasks to conduct during Section 7, although you could begin some End-of-Year tasks toward the end of the section if you worry that you will run out of time or if you need information prior to writing report cards or conducting parent-teacher conferences.

◆ **Looking Ahead** The next periodic assessment will be the End-of-Year Periodic Assessment (see pages 45–48), which occurs during Section 8. The End-of-Year periodic assessment tasks include all of the content covered on the Mid-Year Assessment as well as some additional content.

Assessment Overview

Ongoing Assessment

Ongoing assessment involves observing children during daily activities. The four major ongoing assessment opportunities are Kid-Watching, Recognizing Student Achievement, Informing Instruction, and Portfolio Opportunities.

Be on the lookout for kid-watching opportunities as children do the Ongoing Daily Routines, the Core Activities, and the Teaching Options, as well as at various other times when they use mathematics throughout the day. (See pages 66–75 for specific kid-watching suggestions organized by mathematical strand.)

Recognizing Student Achievement

The information in this chart summarizes the Recognizing Student Achievement (RSA) opportunities that are highlighted in Section 8.

Activity	Content Assessed	Where to Find It
8♦1	**Exchanging 1s for 10s and 10s for 100s** [Number and Numeration Goal 3]	*Ones, Tens, Hundreds* Game (*Teacher's Guide to Activities*, p. 381)
8♦9	**Representing equivalent names for numbers** [Number and Numeration Goal 5]	Name Collection Posters (*Teacher's Guide to Activities*, p. 399)
8♦10	**Applying rules to complete number pairs** [Patterns, Functions, and Algebra Goal 1]	"What's My Rule?" with Numbers (*Teacher's Guide to Activities*, p. 401)
8♦13	**Identifying 2- and 3-dimensional shapes** [Geometry Goal 1]	*I Spy* Game (*Teacher's Guide to Activities*, p. 407)
8♦14	**Identifying addition and subtraction situations** [Operations and Computation Goal 2] **Using +, −, and = symbols to model number stories** [Patterns, Functions, and Algebra Goal 2]	Number Stories with Calculators (*Teacher's Guide to Activities*, p. 408)
8♦15	**Generating equivalent names for numbers** [Number and Numeration Goal 5] **Using addition and subtraction to generate equivalent names for numbers** [Operations and Computation Goal 1]	Number Writing (*Teacher's Guide to Activities*, p. 412)

Informing Instruction

The Informing Instruction (II) opportunities highlight children's thinking and suggest ways to enhance it, as well as ways to avoid misunderstandings. Informing Instruction in Section 8 appears in the following activities: 8-4 and 8-16.

Portfolio Opportunities

The information in this table summarizes the Portfolio Opportunities that are highlighted in Section 8.

Activity	Portfolio Opportunity	What to Look For
8◆9	**Children use writing and drawing to create name-collection posters.** **Collect** Name-Collection Posters or photographs of these posters. (Making Name-Collection Posters Core Activity)	• Does the child use a variety of representations to show equivalent names for numbers?
8◆9	**Children create number scrolls.** **Collect** number scrolls. (Number Scrolling Core Activity)	• What is the highest number on the child's scroll? • Does the child write the numbers correctly and in the correct positions? • Does the child use knowledge of number patterns when filling in his or her scroll?

Periodic Assessment

Periodic assessment occurs at regular intervals during the school year. *Kindergarten Everyday Mathematics* suggests that you conduct Baseline, Mid-Year, and End-of-Year periodic assessment tasks.

◆ **During Section 8** Conduct the End-of-Year Periodic Assessment (see pages 45–48) during Section 8 to help you assess children's level of understanding and their progress with respect to each Kindergarten Goal.

Assessment Overview by Strand

The information in this section highlights the range of assessment options for each of the mathematical skills and concepts that comprise the Kindergarten Goals. The following information is included for each skill or concept that should be assessed:

◆ Column 1 includes the **content assessed** by Kindergarten Goal. See pages 27–33 for a complete list of Kindergarten Goals.

◆ Column 2 includes all of the **ongoing assessment** notes related to the skill or concept.

◆ Column 3 includes information on whether there are Baseline, Mid-Year, and/or End-of-Year periodic assessment suggestions linked to that skill or concept.

◆ Below each table are some examples of how the skill or concept might be assessed through everyday **kid-watching.**

The pages in this section are organized by content strand as follows:

Number and Numeration Assessment Overview

Content Assessed [Kindergarten Goal]	Ongoing Assessment Notes I = Informing Instruction R = Recognizing Student Achievement		Periodic Assessment Suggestions B = Baseline (see pages 40–41) M = Mid-Year (see pages 42–44) E = End-of-Year (see pages 45–48)		
	I	R	B	M	E
Count on by 1s to 100. [Number and Numeration Goal 1]	1♦12 2♦6 2♦11 4♦12 7♦2 7♦7 8♦4	4♦6	●	●	●
Count on by 2s. [Number and Numeration Goal 1]	See kid-watching opportunities on the following page.				●
Count on by 5s. [Number and Numeration Goal 1]	See kid-watching opportunities on the following page.			●	●
Count on by 10s. [Number and Numeration Goal 1]	7♦2	6♦7		●	●
Count back by 1s with number grids, number lines, and calculators. [Number and Numeration Goal 1]	7♦7		●	●	●
Count 20 or more objects. [Number and Numeration Goal 2]	1♦3 7♦2	1♦14 2♦4 3♦1 3♦5 3♦16	●	●	●
Estimate the number of objects in a collection. [Number and Numeration Goal 2]		5♦10		●	●
Model numbers with manipulatives. [Number and Numeration Goal 3]		7♦8		●	●
Use manipulatives to exchange 1s for 10s and 10s for 100. [Number and Numeration Goal 3]	8♦16	7♦8 8♦1			●
Recognize that digits can be used and combined to read and write numbers. [Number and Numeration Goal 3]	2♦7 4♦7 4♦16 7♦10	5♦3		●	●
Read numbers up to 30. [Number and Numeration Goal 3]	1♦5 3♦9	1♦14 2♦4 3♦5 5♦3	●	●	●
Use manipulatives to model half of a region or collection; describe the model. [Number and Numeration Goal 4]	6♦16	7♦4			●
Use manipulatives, drawings, and numerical expressions involving addition and subtraction of 1-digit numbers to give equivalent names for whole numbers up to 20. [Number and Numeration Goal 5]	5♦4	8♦9 8♦15			●
Compare and order whole numbers up to 20. [Number and Numeration Goal 6]	2♦11 3♦6 3♦9 4♦12 5♦15	3♦16 4♦2 7♦14	●	●	●

Number and Numeration Kid-Watching Opportunities

Count on and back by 2s, 5s, and 10s. [Number and Numeration Goal 1] Listen as children count during games such as Hide and Seek, when saying rhymes and chants that use number counts (by 1s, 2s, 5s, or 10s) and when counting up (by 1s, 2s, 5s, or 10s) to the Number of the Day or doing *Minute Math* activities.

Count 20 or more objects. [Number and Numeration Goal 2] Watch children as they do the daily Attendance and Survey Routines (counting children, counting responses), prepare snacks (counting cups and snack items), play games (moving spaces, counting dots on dice, dealing out cards), and during outdoor play (jumping rope, bouncing balls).

Estimate the number of objects in a collection. [Number and Numeration Goal 2] Watch for children estimating the number of children present and absent during the daily Attendance Routine. Listen for children's responses to the *Minute Math* activities related to estimation. Watch children as they get materials or treats to share. Do they get about the right number of pieces of paper to give one to everyone? Do they have enough pretzels to pass out and still have a few left?

Model numbers with manipulatives. [Number and Numeration Goal 3] Watch as children work with the concrete objects for the Number of the Day Routine. Watch children counting objects or drawing pictures to match number posters, number books, or number boards and during many games and Center activities.

Use manipulatives to exchange 1s for 10s and 10s for 100s. [Number and Numeration Goal 3] Watch children during the Concrete Number Count part of the Number of the Day Routine. Also observe them during activities or games which require them to make exchanges (such as Coin Exchange, Tens and Ones with Craft Sticks, or *One Dollar Game*).

Recognize that digits can be used and combined to read and write numbers. Read numbers up to 30. [Number and Numeration Goal 3] Watch children as they read and write numbers during Number of the Day and Attendance Routines, play games such as *Monster Squeeze, Top-It,* and *Double Digits with Dice,* and do activities such as Number Grid, Number Scrolls, Number Stories, and Slate and Calculator Activities.

Use manipulatives to model half of a region or a collection. [Number and Numeration Goal 4] Watch children as they divide themselves equally into teams, share manipulatives during play or Center times, and share snacks. Observe them as they fold paper or cut paper objects in half for art projects. Pose "half" Number Stories and look for *Minute Math* problems that feature the concept of half.

Use manipulatives, drawings, and numerical expressions involving addition and subtraction of 1-digit numbers to give equivalent names for whole numbers up to 20. [Number and Numeration Goal 5] Observe the various ways children name a number using manipulatives (craft sticks, beads, and counters), combinations of dots on dice or dominoes, fingers, drawings, and addition or subtraction expressions. Listen to the language children use to explain the ways they represent a number.

Compare and order whole numbers up to 20. [Number and Numeration Goal 6] Watch whether children can compare numbers as they play games such as *Monster Squeeze, Top-It,* or *Teen Frame,* and during *Minute Math* activities. Children also demonstrate many spontaneous number comparisons during everyday classroom life: *I have more than you. How come you got 9 and I only got 6? Marcus got the most.*

Operations and Computation Assessment Overview

Content Assessed [Kindergarten Goal]	Ongoing Assessment Notes I = Informing Instruction R = Recognizing Student Achievement		Periodic Assessment Suggestions B = Baseline (see pages 40–41) M = Mid-Year (see pages 42–44) E = End-of-Year (see pages 45–48)		
	I	**R**	**B**	**M**	**E**
Use manipulatives, number lines, and mental arithmetic to solve problems involving the addition and subtraction of 1-digit whole numbers. [Operations and Computation Goal 1]	2♦14	7♦6 8♦15		•	•
Identify join and take-away situations. [Operations and Computation Goal 2]	2♦14 3♦13	7♦3 8♦14		•	•

Operations and Computation Kid-Watching Opportunities

Use manipulatives, number lines, and mental arithmetic to solve problems involving the addition and subtraction of 1-digit whole numbers. [Operations and Computation Goal 1] Observe the strategies children use as they solve join (addition) and take-away (subtraction) problems presented in games, Pocket Problems, *Minute Math* activities, or number stories. Do they use manipulatives or fingers, refer to a number line, or use mental math skills to find the solution? Listen to the language children use to explain how they solve problems.

Identify join and take-away situations. [Operations and Computation Goal 2] Watch whether children can identify Pocket Problems, *Minute Math* problems, number stories, and other problems as join (addition) or take-away (subtraction) situations.

Data and Chance Assessment Overview

Content Assessed [Kindergarten Goal]	Ongoing Assessment Notes I = Informing Instruction R = Recognizing Student Achievement		Periodic Assessment Suggestions B = Baseline (see pages 40–41) M = Mid-Year (see pages 42–44) E = End-of-Year (see pages 45–48)		
	I	**R**	**B**	**M**	**E**
Collect and organize data to create class-constructed tally charts, tables, and bar graphs. [Data and Chance Goal 1]	See kid-watching opportunities below.		Not assessed in Periodic Assessment		
Use graphs to answer simple questions. [Data and Chance Goal 2]	3◆14	5◆13			●
Describe events using *certain, possible, impossible,* **and other basic probability terms.** [Data and Chance Goal 3]	3◆11	6◆15		●	●

Data and Chance Kid-Watching Opportunities

Collect and organize data to create class-constructed tally charts, tables, and bar graphs. [Data and Chance Goal 1] Watch how children manage class data during the Attendance Routine, the Weather Routine, the Temperature Routine and the Survey Routine. As children begin to graph their own surveys, observe their data collection and organization skills.

Use graphs to answer simple questions. [Data and Chance Goal 2] Observe children during class graphing activities and discussions about the graphs. Are they able to glean information from the graphs and answer questions based on the graphs?

Describe events using *certain, possible, impossible* **and other basic probability terms.** [Data and Chance Goal 3] Listen for the language that children use to describe the likelihood of events when they are doing the Weather and Temperature Routines and in their play. *(I'm definitely going to see that movie. My mom said there was no chance we could have that cereal. I think I'm going to win.)* Also note whether children incorporate any awareness of probability as they play games with dice, spinners, or other elements of chance.

Measurement and Reference Frames Assessment Overview

Content Assessed [Kindergarten Goal]	Ongoing Assessment Notes I = Informing Instruction R = Recognizing Student Achievement		Periodic Assessment Suggestions B = Baseline (see pages 40–41) M = Mid-Year (see pages 42–44) E = End-of-Year (see pages 45–48)		
	I	**R**	**B**	**M**	**E**
Use nonstandard tools and techniques to estimate and compare weight and length. [Measurement and Reference Frames Goal 1]	1•1 5•11	1•13 6•9	●	●	●
Identify standard measuring tools. [Measurement and Reference Frames Goals 1, 3, and 4]	3•12 5•11	6•9			●
Identify pennies, nickels, dimes, quarters, and dollar bills. [Measurement and Reference Frames Goal 2]		6•8 7•1			●
Describe temperature using appropriate vocabulary terms, such as *hot, warm,* and *cold;* identify a thermometer as a tool for measuring temperature. [Measurement and Reference Frames Goal 3]	See kid-watching opportunities below.		Not assessed in Periodic Assessment		
Describe and use measures of time periods relative to a day and week; identify tools that measure time. [Measurement and Reference Frames Goal 4]		5•1			●

Measurement and Reference Frames Kid-Watching Opportunities

Use nonstandard tools and techniques to estimate and compare weight and length. [Measurement and Reference Frames Goal 1] Watch and listen to children as they play with blocks, work in the Art Center, and describe classroom objects. Listen for comparison phrases such as: *That block is too large. I need a smaller block. My building is taller than yours. I need a longer piece of paper. My string is too short. This book is heavy. That book is light.*

Identify standard measuring tools. [Measurement and Reference Frames Goal 1] Listen for whether children use the names of measurement tools in everyday classroom life, such as: *The clock shows it is 12:00. Time to eat lunch. The thermometer says it's too cold to go outside. I need a ruler to measure this table.*

Identify pennies, nickles, dimes, quarters, and dollar bills. [Measurement and Reference Frames Goal 2] Listen for whether children use names of coins and the dollar in dramatic play (selling and buying at a store, paying at a restaurant, or selling tickets to a play). Watch and listen as children do coin activities and games and respond to *Minute Math* money activities.

Describe temperature using appropriate vocabulary terms, such as *hot*, *warm*, and *cold*; identify a thermometer as a tool for measuring temperature. [Measurement and Reference Frames Goal 3] Observe children as they do the Temperature Routine. Listen for the words they use to describe the temperature. Also note how they use the thermometer.

Describe and use measures of time periods relative to a day and week. [Measurement and Reference Frames Goal 4] Listen as children do the Calendar Routine and report to the class. Listen to children's conversations about their day, such as: *It's almost lunch, and then we go outside. Tomorrow we are going on a field trip.*

Geometry Assessment Overview

Content Assessed [Kindergarten Goal]	Ongoing Assessment Notes I = Informing Instruction R = Recognizing Student Achievement		Periodic Assessment Suggestions B = Baseline (see pages 40–41) M = Mid-Year (see pages 42–44) E = End-of-Year (see pages 45–48)		
	I	R	B	M	E
Identify and describe plane figures including circles, triangles, squares, and rectangles. [Geometry Goal 1]	2•1 4•10 6•6	2•2 4•13 8•13	•	•	•
Identify and describe solid figures, including spheres and cubes. [Geometry Goal 1]	6•6	8•13			•
Identify shapes having line symmetry. [Geometry Goal 2]		2•16	•	•	•

Geometry Kid-Watching Opportunities

Identify and describe plane and solid figures including circles, triangles, squares, rectangles, spheres, and cubes. [Geometry Goal 1] Observe and listen to the language children use to name and describe shapes as they work with attribute blocks and pattern blocks, describe shapes in their environment, do art projects, play games such as *I Spy,* and do *Minute Math* activities.

Identify shapes having line symmetry. [Geometry Goal 2] Ask children whether particular objects are symmetrical as they do art projects, work with attribute blocks and pattern blocks, and describe their environment.

Patterns, Functions, and Algebra Assessment Overview

Content Assessed [Kindergarten Goal]	Ongoing Assessment Notes I = Informing Instruction R = Recognizing Student Achievement		Periodic Assessment Suggestions B = Baseline (see pages 40–41) M = Mid-Year (see pages 42–44) E = End-of-Year (see pages 45–48)		
	I	**R**	**B**	**M**	**E**
Extend, describe, and create visual, rhythmic, and movement patterns. [Patterns, Functions, and Algebra Goal 1]	1♦10	3♦2 4♦5	●	●	●
Use rules to sort and to make patterns. [Patterns, Functions, and Algebra 1]		6♦12	●	●	●
Use rules to play *"What's My Rule?" Fishing* **and other activities.** [Patterns, Functions, and Algebra Goal 1]	5♦14	6♦12 8♦10			●
Read and write expressions and number sentences using the symbols +, −, and =. [Patterns, Functions, and Algebra Goal 2]		7♦3 8♦14			●

Patterns, Functions, and Algebra Kid-Watching Opportunities

Extend, describe, and create visual, rhythmic, and movement patterns. [Patterns, Functions, and Algebra Goal 1] Observe children when they are making patterns using sound and movement activities from *Minute Math,* and using manipulatives such as pattern blocks, attribute blocks, or craft sticks. Note whether children point out patterns in their environment (clothing, artwork, floor tiles, and so on).

Use rules to sort and make patterns. [Patterns, Functions, and Algebra Goal 1] Observe how children (often spontaneously) sort collections of objects when they are playing games, using manipulatives, eating lunch or snacks, or playing outdoors or in the classroom.

Use rules during *What's My Rule? Fishing* and other activities. [Patterns, Functions, and Algebra Goal 1] Observe children as they play *"What's My Rule?" Fishing* or do any other "What's My Rule?" activity, including many activities with attribute blocks. Many commercial games for young children involve identifying and using attribute-based rules.

Read and write expressions and number sentences using the symbols +, −, and =. [Patterns, Functions, and Algebra Goal 2] Watch whether children can use symbols and number sentences in conjunction with number stories, *Minute Math* activities, and activities or games such as Pocket Problems and the *Growing and Disappearing Train Game.*

Assessment Masters

Contents

Ongoing Assessment Tools

Periodic Assessment Tools

Additional Assessment Tools

Name _____ Date _____

Activity	Recognizing Student Achievement	Assess Progress	Comments
1◆13	**Compare lengths of two objects.** [Measurement and Reference Frames Goal 1]		
1◆14	**Count 1–10 objects.** [Number and Numeration Goal 2]		
	Read numbers 1–10. [Number and Numeration Goal 3]		
2◆2	**Identify and name a triangle and circle.** [Geometry Goal 1]		
2◆4	**Count 1–10 objects (spaces).** [Number and Numeration Goal 2]		
	Read numbers 1–10. [Number and Numeration Goal 3]		
2◆16	**Identify symmetrical objects.** [Geometry Goal 2]		

Assess Progress:　**A** = adequate progress　**N** = not adequate progress　**N/A** = not assessed

Kid-Watching Observations

_____

_____

_____

_____

_____

_____

_____

_____

_____

Class _____

Date _____

Names	Compare lengths of two objects. [Measurement and Reference Frames Goal 1] 1•13	Count 1–10 objects. [Number and Numeration Goal 2] Read numbers 1–10. [Number and Numeration Goal 3] 1•14	Identify and name a triangle and circle. [Geometry Goal 1] 2•2	Count 1–10 objects (spaces). [Number and Numeration Goal 2] Read numbers 1–10. [Number and Numeration Goal 3] 2•4	Identify symmetrical objects. [Geometry Goal 2] 2•16	Kid-Watching Observations
1.						
2.						
3.						
4.						
5.						
6.						
7.						
8.						
9.						
10.						
11.						
12.						
13.						
14.						
15.						
16.						
17.						
18.						
19.						
20.						
21.						
22.						
23.						
24.						
25.						

Assess Progress: = adequate progress **N** = not adequate progress **N/A** = not assessed

Name _____   Date _____

Activity	Recognizing Student Achievement	Assess Progress	Comments
3◆1	**Represent numbers 1–10 with objects.** [Number and Numeration Goal 2]		
3◆2	**Create and describe a pattern.** [Patterns, Functions, and Algebra Goal 1]		
3◆5	**Count 1–12 objects.** [Number and Numeration Goal 2]		
	Read numbers 1–12. [Number and Numeration Goal 3]		
3◆16	**Count teen numbers.** [Number and Numeration Goal 2]		
	Compare teen numbers. [Number and Numeration Goal 6]		
4◆2	**Compare numbers 0–20.** [Number and Numeration Goal 6]		
4◆5	**Create, extend, and describe 2- and 3-part patterns.** [Patterns, Functions, and Algebra Goal 1]		
4◆6	**Count by 1s to at least 30.** [Number and Numeration Goal 1]		
	Count backward. [Number and Numeration Goal 1]		
4◆13	**Recognize and name shapes.** [Geometry Goal 1]		
	Use rules to sort a collection of objects. [Patterns, Functions, and Algebra Goal 1]		

Assess Progress: **A** = adequate progress   **N** = not adequate progress   **N/A** = not assessed

Kid-Watching Observations

_____

_____

_____

Class _____

Date _____

Names	Represent numbers 1–10 with objects. [Number and Numeration Goal 2] 3•1	Create and describe a pattern. [Patterns, Functions, and Algebra Goal 1] 3•2	Count 1–12 objects. [Number and Numeration Goal 2] Read numbers 1–12. [Number and Numeration Goal 3] 3•5	Count teen numbers. [Number and Numeration Goal 2] Compare teen numbers. [Number and Numeration Goal 2] 3•16	Compare numbers 0–20. [Number and Numeration Goal 6] 4•2	Create, extend, and describe 2- and 3-part patterns. [Patterns, Functions, and Algebra Goal 1] 4•5	Count by 1s to at least 30. [Number and Numeration Goal 1] Count backward. [Number and Numeration Goal 1] 4•6	Recognize and name shapes. [Geometry Goal 1] Use rules to sort a collection of objects. [Patterns, Functions, and Algebra Goal 1] 4•13	Kid-Watching Observations
1.									
2.									
3.									
4.									
5.									
6.									
7.									
8.									
9.									
10.									
11.									
12.									
13.									
14.									
15.									
16.									
17.									
18.									
19.									
20.									
21.									
22.									
23.									
24.									
25.									

Assess Progress: **A** = adequate progress **N** = not adequate progress **N/A** = not assessed

Individual Profile of Progress:
Ongoing Assessment

Name _____ Date _____

Activity	Recognizing Student Achievement	Assess Progress	Comments
5•1	**Sequence events and describe time periods of the day.** [Measurement and Reference Frames Goal 4]		
5•3	**Read and write 2-digit numbers.** [Number and Numeration Goal 3]		
5•10	**Make reasonable estimates.** [Number and Numeration Goal 2]		
5•13	**Answer questions based on a graph.** [Data and Chance Goal 2]		
6•7	**Count by 10s.** [Number and Numeration Goal 1]		
6•8	**Identify pennies, nickels, and dimes.** [Measurement and Reference Frames Goal 2]		
6•9	**Use nonstandard measuring tools and units to measure length.** [Measurement and Reference Frames Goal 1]		
6•12	**Use attribute rules to find objects.** [Patterns, Functions, and Algebra Goal 1]		
6•15	**Use basic probability terms.** [Data and Chance Goal 3]		

Assess Progress:　**A** = adequate progress　**N** = not adequate progress　**N/A** = not assessed

Kid-Watching Observations

_____

_____

_____

_____

_____

_____

Class _____

Date _____

Names	Sequence events and describe time periods of the day. [Measurement and Reference Frames Goal 4] 5•1	Read and write 2-digit numbers. [Number and Numeration Goal 3] 5•3	Make reasonable estimates. [Number and Numeration Goal 2] 5•10	Answer questions based on a graph. [Data and Chance Goal 2] 5•13	Count by 10s. [Number and Numeration Goal 1] 6•7	Identify pennies, nickels, and dimes. [Measurement and Reference Frames Goal 2] 6•8	Use nonstandard measuring tools and units to measure length. [Measurement and Reference Frames Goal 2] 6•9	Use attribute rules to find objects. [Patterns, Functions, and Algebra Goal 1] 6•12	Use basic probability terms. [Data and Chance Goal 3] 6•15	Kid-Watching Observations
1.										
2.										
3.										
4.										
5.										
6.										
7.										
8.										
9.										
10.										
11.										
12.										
13.										
14.										
15.										
16.										
17.										
18.										
19.										
20.										
21.										
22.										
23.										
24.										
25.										

Assess Progress: **A** = adequate progress   **N** = not adequate progress   **N/A** = not assessed

Name   Date

Activity	Recognizing Student Achievement	Assess Progress	Comments
7◆1	**Identify names and values of coins.** [Measurement and Reference Frames Goal 2]		
7◆3	**Identify addition and subtraction stories.** [Operations and Computation Goal 2]		
	Use +, −, = symbols to represent number stories. [Patterns, Functions, and Algebra Goal 2]		
7◆4	**Model half of a collection.** [Number and Numeration Goal 4]		
7◆6	**Add small numbers.** [Operations and Computation Goal 1]		
7◆8	**Use manipulatives to model numbers and make exchanges.** [Number and Numeration Goal 3]		
7◆14	**Compare and order numbers.** [Number and Numeration Goal 6]		
8◆1	**Exchange 1s for 10s and 10s for 100s.** [Number and Numeration Goal 3]		
8◆9	**Represent equivalent names for numbers.** [Number and Numeration Goal 5]		
8◆10	**Apply rules to complete number pairs.** [Patterns, Functions, and Algebra Goal 1]		
8◆13	**Identify 2- and 3-dimensional shapes.** [Geometry Goal 1]		
8◆14	**Identify addition and subtraction situations.** [Operations and Computation Goal 2]		
	Use +, −, = symbols to model number stories. [Patterns, Functions, and Algebra Goal 2]		
8◆15	**Generate equivalent names for numbers.** [Number and Numeration Goal 5]		
	Use addition and subtraction to generate equivalent names for numbers. [Operations and Computation Goal 1]		

Assess Progress: = adequate progress    = not adequate progress    = not assessed

Sections
7–8

Class Checklist:
Ongoing Assessment

Class ____________________

Date ____________________

Names	7•1	7•3	7•4	7•6	7•8	7•14	8•1	8•9	8•10	8•13	8•14	8•15	Kid-Watching Observations
	Identify names and values of coins. [Measurement and Reference Frames Goal 2]	**Identify addition and subtraction stories.** [Operations and Computation Goal 2] **Use +, −, and = symbols to represent number stories.** [Patterns, Functions, and Algebra Goal 2]	**Model half of a collection.** [Number and Numeration Goal 4]	**Add small numbers.** [Operations and Computation Goal 1]	**Use manipulatives to model numbers and make exchanges.** [Number and Numeration Goal 3]	**Compare and order numbers.** [Number and Numeration Goal 6]	**Exchange 1s for 10s and 10s for 100s.** [Number and Numeration Goal 3]	**Represent equivalent names for numbers.** [Number and Numeration Goal 5]	**Apply rules to complete number pairs.** [Patterns, Functions, and Algebra Goal 1]	**Identify 2- and 3-dimensional shapes.** [Geometry Goal 1]	**Identify addition and subtraction situations.** [Operations and Computation Goal 2] **Use +, −, and = symbols to model number stories.** [Patterns, Functions, and Algebra Goal 2]	**Generate equivalent names for numbers.** [Number and Numeration Goal 5] **Use addition and subtraction to generate equivalent names for numbers.** [Operations and computation Goal 1]	
1.													
2.													
3.													
4.													
5.													
6.													
7.													
8.													
9.													
10.													
11.													
12.													
13.													
14.													
15.													
16.													
17.													
18.													
19.													
20.													
21.													
22.													
23.													
24.													
25.													

Assess Progress: **A** = adequate progress **N** = not adequate progress **N/A** = not assessed

Name _____   Date _____

Tasks	Content Assessed	Child's Responses	Comments
1	**Count on by 1s.** [Number and Numeration Goal 1]	Counts on to _____.	
2	**Count back by 1s.** [Number and Numeration Goal 1]	Counts back from _____.	
3	**Count objects.** [Number and Numeration Goal 2]	Counts _____ objects.	
4	**Read numbers.** [Number and Numeration Goal 3]	Numbers read: _____ _____ _____	
5	**Compare and order numbers.** [Number and Numeration Goal 6]	Range of numbers compared: _____	
6	**Compare sizes of objects.** [Measurement and Reference Frames Goal 1]	Size comparison language used: _____ _____ _____	
7	**Recognize 2-dimensional geometric shapes.** [Geometry Goal 1]	Recognizes: Circle _____ Triangle _____ Square _____ Rectangle _____	
8	**Identify shapes having line symmetry.** [Geometry Goal 2]	Objects used: _____ Recognizes matching sides? _____	
9	**Extend a pattern.** [Patterns, Functions, and Algebra Goal 1]	Pattern used: _____ Extends? _____	
10	**Use a rule to sort objects.** [Patterns, Functions, and Algebra Goal 1]	Sorts by rule? _____ Rule used: _____	

Baseline Periodic Assessment

Class Checklist

Class _____

Date _____

Names	1. Count on by 1s to ___. [Number and Numeration Goal 1]	2. Count back by 1s from ___. [Number and Numeration Goal 1]	3. Count ___ objects. [Number and Numeration Goal 2]	4. Read numbers. [Number and Numeration Goal 3]	5. Compare and order numbers. [Number and Numeration Goal 6]	6. Compare sizes of objects. [Measurement and Reference Frames Goal 1]	7. Recognize 2-dimensional geometric shapes. [Geometry Goal 1]	8. Identify shapes having line symmetry. [Geometry Goal 2]	9. Extend a pattern. [Patterns, Functions, and Algebra Goal 1]	10. Use a rule to sort objects. [Patterns, Functions, and Algebra Goal 1]
1.										
2.										
3.										
4.										
5.										
6.										
7.										
8.										
9.										
10.										
11.										
12.										
13.										
14.										
15.										
16.										
17.										
18.										
19.										
20.										
21.										
22.										
23.										
24.										
25.										

Individual Profile of Progress

Name _____   Date _____

Task	Content Assessed	Child's Responses	Assess Progress	Comments
1	**Count on by 1s.** [Number and Numeration Goal 1]	Counts on to _____.		
2	**Count back by 1s.** [Number and Numeration Goal 1]	Counts back from _____.		
3a	**Count on by 5s.** [Number and Numeration Goal 1]	Counts on to _____.		
3b	**Count on by 10s.** [Number and Numeration Goal 1]	Counts on to _____.		
4	**Count objects.** [Number and Numeration Goal 2]	Counts _____ objects.		
5	**Estimate the number of objects in a collection.** [Number and Numeration Goal 2]	Understands concept of estimation? _____		
6	**Model numbers with manipulatives.** [Number and Numeration Goal 3]	Numbers modeled: _____ _____ _____		
7	**Read and write (or dictate) 2-digit numbers.** [Number and Numeration Goal 3]	Range of numbers read and written (or dictated): _____ _____ _____		
8	**Compare and order numbers.** [Number and Numeration Goal 6]	Range of numbers compared: _____ _____ _____		
9a	**Solve number stories.** [Operations and Computation Goal 1]	Problem solved: _____ _____ _____ Strategies: _____ _____		

Assess Progress: = adequate progress    = not adequate progress   = not assessed

Name _____ Date _____

Task	Content Assessed	Child's Responses	Assess Progress	Comments
9b	**Identify join and take-away situations.** [Operations and Computation Goal 2]	Identifies: Join _____ Take-away _____		
10	**Describe events using basic probability terms.** [Data and Chance Goal 3]	Terms used: _____ _____ _____		
11	**Use nonstandard tools and techniques to estimate and compare weight and length.** [Measurement and Reference Frames Goal 1]	Compare length? _____ Compare weight? _____ Tools used: _____ _____		
12	**Identify 2-dimensional geometric shapes.** [Geometry Goal 1]	Identifies: Circle _____ Triangle _____ Square _____ Rectangle _____		
13	**Identify shapes having line symmetry.** [Geometry Goal 2]	Objects used: _____ Recognizes line symmetry? _____		
14	**Extend, describe, and create patterns.** [Patterns, Functions, and Algebra Goal 1]	Extends: _____ Describes: _____ Creates (show pattern): _____		
15	**Use a rule to sort objects.** [Patterns, Functions, and Algebra Goal 1]	Sorts by specified rule? _____ Rule used: _____ Sorts by self-chosen rule? _____ Rule used: _____		

Assess Progress: **A** = adequate progress   **N** = not adequate progress   **N/A** = not assessed

Class Checklist

Class _____

Date _____

Names	1. Count on by 1s to ___. [Number and Numeration Goal 1]	2. Count back by 1s from ___. [Number and Numeration Goal 1]	3a. Count on by 5s to ___. [Number and Numeration Goal 1]	3b. Count on by 10s to ___. [Number and Numeration Goal 1]	4. Count ___ objects. [Number and Numeration Goal 2]	5. Estimate the number of objects in a collection. [Number and Numeration Goal 2]	6. Model numbers with manipulatives. [Number and Numeration Goal 3]	7. Read and write (or dictate) 2-digit numbers to ___. [Number and Numeration Goal 3]
1.								
2.								
3.								
4.								
5.								
6.								
7.								
8.								
9.								
10.								
11.								
12.								
13.								
14.								
15.								
16.								
17.								
18.								
19.								
20.								
21.								
22.								
23.								
24.								
25.								

Assess Progress: A = adequate progress  N = not adequate progress N/A = not assessed

Class Checklist *cont.*

Class _____

Date _____

Names	8. Compare and order numbers to ___. [Number and Numeration Goal 6]	9a. Solve number stories. [Operations and Computation Goal 1]	9b. Identify join and take-away situations. [Operations and Computation Goal 1]	10. Describe events using basic probability terms. [Data and Chance Goal 3]	11. Use nonstandard tools and techniques to estimate and compare weight and length. [Measurement and Reference Frames Goal 1]	12. Identify 2-dimensional geometric shapes. [Geometry Goal 1]	13. Identify shapes having line symmetry. [Geometry Goal 2]	14. Extend, describe, and create patterns. [Patterns, Functions, and Algebra Goal 1]	15. Use a rule to sort objects. [Patterns, Functions, and Algebra Goal 1]
1.									
2.									
3.									
4.									
5.									
6.									
7.									
8.									
9.									
10.									
11.									
12.									
13.									
14.									
15.									
16.									
17.									
18.									
19.									
20.									
21.									
22.									
23.									
24.									
25.									

Assess Progress: **A** = adequate progress   **N** = not adequate progress   **N/A** = not assessed

Individual Profile of Progress

Name _____ Date _____

Tasks	Content Assessed	Child's Responses	Assess Progress	Comments
1	**Count on by 1s.** [Number and Numeration Goal 1]	Counts on to _____.		
2	**Count back by 1s.** [Number and Numeration Goal 1]	Counts back from _____.		
3a	**Count on by 2s.** [Number and Numeration Goal 1]	Counts on to _____.		
3b	**Count on by 5s.** [Number and Numeration Goal 1]	Counts on to _____.		
3c	**Count on by 10s.** [Number and Numeration Goal 1]	Counts on to _____.		
4	**Count objects.** [Number and Numeration Goal 2]	Counts _____ objects.		
5	**Estimate the number of objects in a collection.** [Number and Numeration Goal 2]	Understands concept of estimation? _____		
6	**Model numbers with manipulatives.** [Number and Numeration Goal 3]	Numbers modeled: _____ _____ _____		
7	**Exchange 1s for 10s and 10s for 100.** [Number and Numeration Goal 3]	Understands 1s for 10 exchange? _____ Understands 10s for 100 exchange? _____		
8	**Read and write (or dictate) 2-digit numbers.** [Number and Numeration Goal 3]	Range of numbers read and written (or dictated): _____ _____ _____		
9	**Use manipulatives to model half of a region or collection.** [Number and Numeration Goal 4]	Understands half? _____		

Assess Progress:  **A** = adequate progress  **N** = not adequate progress   **N/A** = not assessed

Name _____   Date _____

Task	Content Assessed	Child's Responses	Assess Progress	Comments
10	**Give equivalent names for numbers.** [Number and Numeration Goal 5]	Number given: _____ Some equivalent names given: _____ _____ _____		
11	**Compare and order numbers.** [Number and Numeration Goal 6]	Range of numbers compared: _____		
12a	**Solve number stories.** [Operations and Computation Goal 1]	Problem solved: _____ _____ Strategies: _____ _____		
12b	**Identify join and take-away situations.** [Operations and Computation Goal 2]	Identifies: Join _____ Take-away _____		
12c	**Read and write expressions and number sentences using the symbols +, −, and =.** [Patterns, Functions, and Algebra Goal 2]	Uses symbols correctly: + _____ − _____ = _____		
13	**Use graphs to answer simple questions.** [Data and Chance Goal 2]	Questions answered: _____ _____		
14	**Describe events using basic probability terms.** [Data and Chance Goal 3]	Terms used: _____ _____ _____		

Assess Progress: **A** = adequate progress   **N** = not adequate progress   **N/A** = not assessed

Name _____ Date _____

Task	Content Assessed	Child's Responses	Assess Progress	Comments
15	**Use nonstandard tools and techniques to estimate and compare weight and length.** [Measurement and Reference Frames Goal 1]	Compare length? _____ Compare weight? _____ Tools used: _____ _____		
16	**Identify pennies, nickels, dimes, quarters, and dollar bills.** [Measurement and Reference Frames Goal 2]	Penny _____ Nickel _____ Dime _____ Quarter _____ Dollar bill _____		
17	**Identify standard measuring tools.** [Measurement and Reference Frames Goals 1, 3, and 4]	Tools Identified: Ruler _____ Pan balance _____ Clock _____ Thermometer _____		
18	**Describe and use time periods relative to a day and week.** [Measurement and Reference Frames Goal 4]	Terms used: _____ _____ _____		
19a	**Identify 2-dimensional geometric shapes.** [Geometry Goal 1]	Identifies: Circle _____ Triangle _____ Square _____ Rectangle _____		
19b	**Identify 3-dimensional geometric solids.** [Geometry Goal 1]	Identifies: Cube _____ Sphere _____		

Assess Progress:  **A** = adequate progress **N** = not adequate progress **N/A** = not assessed

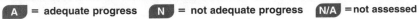

Individual Profile of Progress *cont.*

Name _____   Date _____

Task	Content Assessed	Child's Responses	Assess Progress	Comments
20	**Identify shapes having line symmetry.** [Geometry Goal 2]	Objects used: _____ Recognizes line symmetry? _____		
21	**Extend, describe, and create patterns.** [Patterns, Functions, and Algebra Goal 1]	Extends: _____ Describes: _____ Creates (show pattern): _____		
22	**Use a rule to sort objects.** [Patterns, Functions, and Algebra Goal 1]	Sorts by different rules? _____		
23	**Use rules for *"What's My Rule?"* *Fishing* and other activities.** [Patterns, Functions, and Algebra Goal 1]	Understands "What's My Rule?" activities? _____		

Assess Progress: **A** = adequate progress   **N** = not adequate progress   **N/A** = not assessed

Notes

_____
_____
_____
_____
_____
_____
_____
_____
_____
_____
_____

Class Checklist

Class _____

Date _____

Names	1. Count on by 1s to ___. [Number and Numeration Goal 1]	2. Count back by 1s from ___. [Number and Numeration Goal 1]	3a. Count on by 2s. [Number and Numeration Goal 1]	3b. Count on by 5s. [Number and Numeration Goal 1]	3c. Count on by 10s. [Number and Numeration Goal 1]	4. Count objects. [Number and Numeration Goal 1]	5. Estimate the number of objects in a collection. [Number and Numeration Goal 2]	6. Model numbers with manipulatives. [Number and Numeration Goal 3]	7. Exchange 1s for 10s and 10s for 100. [Number and Numeration Goal 3]	8. Read and write (or dictate) 2-digit numbers to ___. [Number and Numeration Goal 3]	9. Use manipulatives to model half of a region or collection. [Number and Numeration Goal 3]	10. Give equivalent names for numbers. [Number and Numeration Goal 4]	11. Compare and order numbers. [Number and Numeration Goal 5]	12a. Solve number stories. [Operations and Computation Goal 6]	12b. Identify join and take-away situations. [Operations and Computation Goal 1]
1.															
2.															
3.															
4.															
5.															
6.															
7.															
8.															
9.															
10.															
11.															
12.															
13.															
14.															
15.															
16.															
17.															
18.															
19.															
20.															
21.															
22.															
23.															
24.															
25.															

Assess Progress: **A** = adequate progress   **N** = not adequate progress   **N/A** = not assessed

Class _____

Date _____

Names	12c. Read and write expressions and number sentences using the symbols +, −, and =. [Patterns, Functions, and Algebra Goal 2]	13. Use graphs to answer simple questions. [Data and Chance Goal 2]	14. Describe events using basic probability terms. [Data and Chance Goal 3]	15. Use nonstandard tools and techniques to estimate and compare weight and length. [Measurement and Reference Frames Goal 1]	16. Identify pennies, nickels, dimes, quarters, and dollar bills. [Measurement and Reference Frames Goal 2]	17. Identify standard measuring tools. [Measurement and Reference Frames Goals 1, 3, and 4]	18. Describe and use time periods relative to a day and week. [Measurement and Reference Frames Goal 4]	19a. Identify 2-dimensional geometric shapes. [Geometry Goal 1]	19b. Identify 3-dimensional geometric solids. [Geometry Goal 1]	20. Identify shapes having line symmetry. [Geometry Goal 2]	21. Extend, describe, and create patterns. [Patterns, Functions, and Algebra Goal 1]	22. Use a rule to sort objects. [Patterns, Functions, and Algebra Goal 1]	23. Use rules for "What's My Rule" Fishing. [Patterns, Functions, and Algebra Goal 1]
1.													
2.													
3.													
4.													
5.													
6.													
7.													
8.													
9.													
10.													
11.													
12.													
13.													
14.													
15.													
16.													
17.													
18.													
19.													
20.													
21.													
22.													
23.													
24.													
25.													

Assess Progress: **A** = adequate progress   **N** = not adequate progress   **N/A** = not assessed

Cumulative Individual Profile of Progress

Name _____ Date _____

Content Assessed (Kindergarten Goal)	Baseline Periodic Assessment Date:	Mid-Year Periodic Assessment Date:	Recognizing Student Achievement Activities
Count on by 1s. [Number and Numeration Goal 1]	Counts on to _____ .	Counts on to _____ .	4◆6 _____
Count back by 1s. [Number and Numeration Goal 1]	Counts back from _____	Counts back from _____ .	
Count on by 5s. [Number and Numeration Goal 1]		Counts on to _____ .	
Count on by 10s. [Number and Numeration Goal 1]		Counts on to _____ .	
Count objects. [Number and Numeration Goal 2]	Counts _____ objects.	Counts _____ objects.	1◆14 _____ 2◆4 _____ 3◆1 _____ 3◆5 _____ 3◆16 _____
Estimate the number of objects in a collection. [Number and Numeration Goal 2]		Understands concept of estimation? _____	
Model numbers with manipulatives. [Number and Numeration Goal 3]		Numbers modeled: _____ _____ _____	
Read and write (or dictate) 2-digit numbers. [Number and Numeration Goal 3]	Numbers read: _____ _____ _____	Range of numbers read and written (or dictated): _____ _____	1◆14 _____ 2◆4 _____ 3◆5 _____
Compare and order numbers. [Number and Numeration Goal 6]	Range of numbers compared: _____	Range of numbers compared: ____ _____	3◆16 _____ 4◆2 _____
Solve number stories. [Operations and Computation Goal 1]		Problems solved: _____ _____ Strategies: _____ _____	

Name _____ Date _____

Content Assessed (Kindergarten Goal)	Baseline Periodic Assessment Date:	Mid-Year Periodic Assessment Date:	Recognizing Student Achievement Activities
Identify join and take-away situations. [Operations and Computation Goal 2]		Identifies: Join _____ Take-away _____	
Describe events using basic probability terms. [Data and Chance Goal 3]		Terms used: _____ _____ _____	
Use nonstandard tools and techniques to estimate and compare weight and length. [Measurement and Reference Frames Goal 1]	Compare length? _____ Compare weight? _____ Tools used: _____ _____	Compare length? _____ Compare weight? _____ Tools used: _____ _____	1◆13 _____
Identify plane (2-dimensional) figures. [Geometry Goal 1]	Recognizes: Circle _____ Triangle _____ Square _____ Rectangle _____	Identifies: Circle _____ Triangle _____ Square _____ Rectangle _____	2◆2 _____ 4◆13 _____
Identify shapes having line symmetry. [Geometry Goal 2]	Objects used: _____ Recognizes matching sides? _____	Objects used: _____ Recognizes line symmetry? _____	2◆16 _____
Extend, describe, and create a pattern. [Patterns, Functions, and Algebra Goal 1]	Pattern used: _____ Extends: _____	Extends: _____ Describes: _____ Creates (show pattern): _____	3◆2 _____ 4◆5 _____
Use a rule to sort objects. [Patterns, Functions, and Algebra Goal 1]	Sorts by rule? _____ Rule used: _____	Sorts by specified rule? _____ Sorts by self-chosen rule? _____	

Cumulative Individual Profile of Progress

Name _____   Date _____

Content Assessed (Kindergarten Goal)	Mid-Year Periodic Assessment Date:	End-of-Year Periodic Assessment Date:	Recognizing Student Achievement Activities
Count on by 1s. [Number and Numeration Goal 1]	Counts on to _____ .	Counts on to _____ .	
Count back by 1s. [Number and Numeration Goal 1]	Counts back from _____ .	Counts back from _____ .	
Count on by 2s. [Number and Numeration Goal 1]		Counts on to _____ .	
Count on by 5s. [Number and Numeration Goal 1]	Counts on to _____ .	Counts on to _____ .	
Count on by 10s. [Number and Numeration Goal 1]	Counts on to _____ .	Counts on to _____ .	
Count objects. [Number and Numeration Goal 2]	Counts _____ objects.	Counts _____ objects.	
Estimate the number of objects in a collection. [Number and Numeration Goal 2]	Understands concept of estimation? _____	Understands concept of estimation? _____	5◆10 _____
Model numbers with manipulatives. [Number and Numeration Goal 3]	Numbers modeled: _____ _____ _____	Numbers modeled: _____ _____ _____	7◆8 _____
Exchange 1s for 10s and 10s for 100. [Number and Numeration Goal 3]		Understands 1s for 10s exchange? _____ Understands 10s for 100s exchange? _____	7◆8 _____ 8◆1 _____
Read and write (or dictate) 2-digit numbers. [Number and Numeration Goal 3]	Range of numbers read and written (or dictated): _____ _____ _____	Range of numbers read and written (or dictated): _____ _____ _____	5◆3 _____

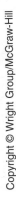

Copyright © Wright Group/McGraw-Hill

Name _____ Date _____

Content Assessed (Kindergarten Goal)	Mid-Year Periodic Assessment Date:	End-of-Year Periodic Assessment Date:	Recognizing Student Achievement Activities
Use manipulatives to model half of a region or collection. [Number and Numeration Goal 4]		Understands half? _____	7◆4 _____
Give equivalent names for numbers. [Number and Numeration Goal 5]		Number given: _____ Some equivalent names given: _____ _____	8◆9 _____ 8◆15 _____
Compare and order numbers. [Number and Numeration Goal 6]	Range of numbers compared: _____	Range of numbers compared: _____ _____	7◆14 _____
Solve number stories. [Operations and Computation Goal 1]	Problem solved: _____ _____ _____ Strategies: _____ _____	Problems solved: _____ _____ _____ Strategies: _____ _____	7◆6 _____ 8◆15 _____
Identify join and take-away situations. [Operations and Computation Goal 2]	Identifies: Join _____ Take-away _____	Identifies: Join _____ Take-away _____	7◆3 _____ 8◆14 _____
Use graphs to answer simple questions. [Data and Chance Goal 2]		Questions answered: _____ _____ _____	5◆13 _____

Name _____   Date _____

Content Assessed (Kindergarten Goal)	Mid-Year Periodic Assessment Date:	End-of-Year Periodic Assessment Date:	Recognizing Student Achievement Activities
Describe events using basic probability terms. [Data and Chance Goal 3]	Terms used: _____ _____ _____	Terms used: _____ _____ _____	6◆15 _____
Use nonstandard tools and techniques to estimate and compare weight and length. [Measurement and Reference Frames Goal 1]	Compare length? _____ Compare weight? _____ Tools used: _____ _____	Compare length? _____ Compare weight? _____ Tools used: _____ _____	6◆9 _____
Identify standard measuring tools. [Measurement and Reference Frames Goals 1, 3, and 4]		Tools Identified: Ruler _____ Pan-balance _____ Clock _____ Thermometer _____	6◆9 _____
Identify pennies, nickels, dimes, quarters, and dollar bills. [Measurement and Reference Frames Goal 2]		Penny _____ Nickel _____ Dime _____ Quarter _____ Dollar bill _____	6◆8 _____ 7◆1 _____
Describe and use time periods relative to a day and week. [Measurement and Reference Frames Goal 4]		Terms used: _____ _____ _____	5◆1 _____

Name _____   Date _____

Content Assessed (Kindergarten Goal)	Mid-Year Periodic Assessment Date:	End-of-Year Periodic Assessment Date:	Recognizing Student Achievement Activities
Identify 2-dimensional geometric shapes. [Geometry Goal 1]	Identifies: Circle _____ Triangle _____ Square _____ Rectangle _____	Identifies: Circle _____ Triangle _____ Square _____ Rectangle _____	8◆13 _____
Identify 3-dimensional geometric solids. [Geometry Goal 1]		Identifies: Cube _____ Sphere _____	8◆13 _____
Identify shapes having line symmetry. [Geometry Goal 2]	Objects used: _____ Recognizes line symmetry? _____	Objects used: _____ Recognizes line symmetry? _____	
Extend, describe, and create patterns. [Patterns, Functions, and Algebra Goal 1]	Extends: _____ Describes: _____ Creates (show pattern): _____	Extends: _____ Describes: _____ Creates (show pattern): _____	
Use a rule to sort objects. [Patterns, Functions, and Algebra Goal 1]	Sorts by specified rule? _____ Rule used: _____ Sorts by self-chosen rule? _____ Rule used: _____	Sorts by different rules? _____	6◆12 _____
Use rules for "What's My Rule?" Fishing and other activities. [Patterns, Functions, and Algebra Goal 1]		Rule used: _____	6◆12 _____ 8◆10 _____
Read and write expressions and number sentences using the symbols +, −, and =. [Patterns, Functions, and Algebra Goal 2]		Uses symbols correctly: + _____ − _____ = _____	7◆3 _____ 8◆14 _____

Name _____   Date _____

Good Work!

🙂 I like this work because

_____

_____

_____

_____

_____

_____

_____

_____

_____

_____

_____

_____

_____

_____

_____

_____

_____

Use as needed.

Parent Reflections

Use the following questions as you tell us how you see your child progressing in mathematics.

What evidence do you see of your child using mathematics at home?

What do you think are your child's strengths and challenges in mathematics?

What thoughts do you have about your child's progress in mathematics?

_____

_____

_____

_____

_____

_____

_____

_____

_____

_____

_____

_____

_____

_____

_____

_____

_____

_____

Class Progress Indicator

Content Assessed	Not Making Adequate Progress	Making Adequate Progress	Exceeding Adequate Progress
Content Assessed: _____ _____ _____ **Dates:** _____ _____	Benchmark: _____	Benchmark: _____	Benchmark: _____
Content Assessed: _____ _____ _____ **Dates:** _____ _____	Benchmark: _____	Benchmark: _____	Benchmark: _____
Content Assessed: _____ _____ _____ **Dates:** _____ _____	Benchmark: _____	Benchmark: _____	Benchmark: _____
Content Assessed: _____ _____ _____ **Dates:** _____ _____	Benchmark: _____	Benchmark: _____	Benchmark: _____

* See pages 16–20 for suggestions about using this sheet.

Class Checklist

Class _____

Date _____

Names										
1.										
2.										
3.										
4.										
5.										
6.										
7.										
8.										
9.										
10.										
11.										
12.										
13.										
14.										
15.										
16.										
17.										
18.										
19.										
20.										
21.										
22.										
23.										
24.										
25.										

* See pages 16–20 for suggestions about using this sheet.

Observation Sheet

Child's Name _____

Assessment Opportunity	Observations
Date and context: _____ _____ _____ _____ _____	_____ _____ _____ _____ _____ _____ _____
Date and context: _____ _____ _____ _____ _____ _____	_____ _____ _____ _____ _____ _____ _____
Date and context: _____ _____ _____ _____ _____ _____	_____ _____ _____ _____ _____ _____ _____
Date and context: _____ _____ _____ _____ _____ _____	_____ _____ _____ _____ _____ _____ _____

* See pages 16–20 for suggestions about using this sheet.

Glossary

Assessment Management System An online management system designed to track student, class, school, and district progress toward Grade-Level Goals. A brief description of this technology begins on page 21 of this handbook.

Class Checklists Recording tools that can be used to keep track of a class's progress on specific Grade-Level Goals.

Content for Assessment Material that is important for children to learn and is the focus of assessment. *Everyday Mathematics* highlights this content through Grade-Level Goals.

Contexts for Assessment Ongoing, periodic, and external assessments based on products or observations.

Enrichment activities Optional activities that apply or deepen children's understanding.

Evidence from Assessment Information about children's knowledge, skills, and dispositions collected from observations or products.

External Assessments Assessments that are completely independent of the curriculum, for example, standardized tests.

Formative Assessments Assessments that provide information about children's current knowledge and abilities so that teachers can plan future instruction more effectively and so that children can identify their own areas of weakness or strength.

Good Work Master A template on which children write about the work they have selected to keep in their portfolios. The master can be found on page 103 of this handbook.

Grade-Level Goals Mathematical goals organized by content strand and articulated across grade levels from Kindergarten through Grade 6.

Individual Profile of Progress A recording tool that can be used to keep track of children's progress on specific Grade-Level Goals.

Informing Instruction note These notes in the *Teacher's Guide to Activities* suggest how to use observations of children's work to adapt instruction by describing common errors and misconceptions in children's thinking and alerting teachers to multiple solution strategies or unique insights children might offer.

Kid-Watching The observing and recording of children's interactions and communications during regular instructional activities.

Making Adequate Progress On a trajectory to meet a Grade-Level Goal.

Observational Assessments Assessments based on observing children during daily activities or periodic assessments.

Ongoing Assessments Assessments based on children's everyday work during regular classroom instruction.

Parent Reflections Page Master A template for collecting parent feedback that can potentially be included in a portfolio of children's work. The master can be found on page 104 of this handbook.

Periodic Assessments Formal assessment events that are built into a curriculum, such as the Kindergarten Baseline, Mid-Year, and End-of-Year assessment tasks.

Portfolios Collections of student products and records of observations which provide opportunities for children to reflect on their mathematical growth and help teachers understand and document that growth.

Product Assessments Assessments based on children's work from daily activities or from periodic assessments.

Program Evaluation Assessment intended to reveal how well a program of instruction is working. A school district, for example, might carry out program evaluation in order to identify schools with especially strong mathematics programs so that their success can be replicated.

Program Goals The fifteen cross-grade goals in *Everyday Mathematics* that weave the program together across grade levels. They form an organizing framework that supports both curriculum and assessment. Every Grade-Level Goal is linked to a Program Goal.

Purposes of Assessment The reasons for assessment, which include providing information that can be used to plan future instruction, identifying what students have achieved during a period of time, and evaluating the quality of the mathematics program.

Readiness Activities Optional activities that preview main activity content or provide alternative routes of access for learning concepts and skills.

Recognizing Student Achievement Note A feature in many activities that highlights specific tasks that can be used to monitor children's progress toward Grade-Level Goals. The notes identify the expectations for a child who is making adequate progress and point to skills or strategies that some children might be able to demonstrate.

Summative Assessments Assessments that aim to measure children's growth and achievement, for example, an assessment to determine whether children have learned certain material by the end of a fixed period of study such as a school-year, a semester or a course.

Index

Name _____ Date _____

Notes

Name _____ Date _____

Notes

_____

_____

_____

_____

_____

_____

_____

_____

_____

_____

_____

_____

_____

_____

_____

Name _____ Date _____

Notes

_____

_____

_____

_____

_____

_____

_____

_____

_____

_____

_____

_____

_____

_____

_____

_____

Notes

Name _____   Date _____

Notes

_____

_____

_____

_____

_____

_____

_____

_____

_____

_____

_____

_____

_____

_____

_____

_____